Fundamentals of
LOGIC

PRENTICE-HALL PHILOSOPHY SERIES
Arthur E. Murphy, Ph.D., *Editor*

Fundamentals of
LOGIC

Arthur Smullyan
Chairman and Professor, Department of
Philosophy □ University of Washington

Prentice-Hall, Inc.
Englewood Cliffs, New Jersey □ □ □ 1962

PRENTICE-HALL INTERNATIONAL, INC.
London   Tokyo   Sydney   Paris
PRENTICE-HALL OF CANADA, LTD.
PRENTICE-HALL DE MEXICO, S.A.

To my wife

Library of Congress Catalog Card Number 62-16662
Printed in the United States of America.   34070C

Acknowledgments

The pages that follow have been so influenced by the work of so many that I do not know where to begin to acknowledge indebtedness. Any uncertainty about my indebtedness to the works of others, however, does not pertain to the writings of W. V. Quine and Alonzo Church. I have frequently consulted their books over the years and my errors would be greater, did I not have their writings to study.

The two chapters on probability rely mainly on traditional materials. It will be obvious that Braithwaite's discussion of the law of large numbers has been very helpful to me. Less obviously, but quite surely, I owe very much to my former teachers, C. I. Lewis, Donald Williams and Ernes Nagel. My colleague, Professor David Keyt, has made many very helpful suggestions on numerous occasions.   ARTHUR SMULLYAN

Table of Contents

Introduction □ 1

What is logic? Principal divisions of logic. Arguments and argument forms. Validity, soundness and rigor. Validating argument forms. Why logic is formal. Elementary and non-elementary statement forms.

PART 1 □ PROOF

Elementary Validating Forms of Argument □ 9

Truth functions. Tautologies. The fundamental principle. Omniparence. Inconsistency. Derivability. Principle of truth functionality. Deletion rules. Countersets.

1

Fundamentals of
LOGIC

Introduction

Logic is the theory of argument. The logician classifies arguments according to type and attempts to express criteria by which the correctness of the various types of arguments can be determined.

Logic may be divided into two principal divisions. The first division is the study of conclusive argument or *proof*. The second division of the subject is the study of relatively inconclusive argument or *confirmation*. Accordingly, Part 1 of this book is the study of arguments which, though not conclusive, still possess varying degrees of cogency.

An argument is a symbolic arrangement in which certain statements, called premisses, are placed in support of other statements, which are called conclusions of the argument.

There exist in everyday language many ways of arranging statements so that some of them are recognizably placed in support

1

of others. We shall adopt one of these methods as standard. We shall express arguments in this way:

$$A_1$$
$$A_2$$
.
.
.
$$\frac{A_i}{B}$$

The statements A_1, A_2, ..., A_i above the line are premisses of the argument. The statement B below the line is called the conclusion of the argument.

It is necessary, in the case of arguments which purport to be conclusive, to distinguish the concepts of validity, soundness, and rigor. The validity of an argument amounts to this: it would be a contradiction in terms for its premisses to be true and its conclusion false. The premisses of a valid argument logically imply the conclusion. The conclusion follows from the premisses of a valid argument. These are alternative and equivalent ways of saying what we mean by a valid argument. We do not apply the term "valid" to statements, but only to arguments. Statements are classified as true or false, and the terms "truth" and "falsity" are not to be applied to arguments.

A sound argument is a valid argument with true premisses. Hence, a sound argument must be valid, but a valid argument need not be sound. We shall ordinarily discuss the validity of an argument rather than the soundness of it. Normally, we are, as logicians, concerned to investigate not the material truth of a set of assumptions but the consequences which logically follow from them.

A rigorous argument is a valid argument which is correctly annotated. The annotation of an argument is not a part of the argument. It is a gloss, or commentary, which explains the steps and cites the logical principles by which we may justify the advance from the premisses to the conclusion of the argument. A rigorous argument must be valid. But a valid argument need not be rigorous, for it may not be annotated, or its annotation may not be correct. Logic seeks general methods for distinguishing between valid and invalid arguments. It seeks also to formulate the principles which are used in the construction and criticism of the annotations of arguments.

We are familiar with the idea that different arguments may have the same form. Thus:

I

IF JONES LIVES IN COLUMBUS, JONES LIVES IN OHIO.

JONES LIVES IN COLUMBUS.

JONES LIVES IN OHIO.

II

IF THE SUM OF THE SQUARES OF THE SIDES OF A RIGHT TRIANGLE EQUALS THE SQUARE OF THE HYPOTENUSE, THEN THE SQUARE OF THE SIN OF AN ANGLE PLUS THE SQUARE OF ITS COSIN IS EQUAL TO 1. THE SUM OF THE SQUARES OF THE SIDES OF A RIGHT TRIANGLE DOES EQUAL THE SQUARE OF THE HYPOTENUSE.

THE SQUARE OF THE SIN OF AN ANGLE PLUS THE SQUARE OF ITS COSIN IS EQUAL TO 1.

It is intuitive that these arguments are both valid and are both of the form:

III

IF A THEN B

A

B

III may be construed as a diagram depicting structural characteristics common to I and II and to countless other arguments as well. We do not call III an argument but an argument form. I and II may be called substitution instances of this argument form, for we obtain these arguments by substituting specific sentences for the variables in III. We note further that III has this characteristic: that all of its substitution instances are valid arguments. An argument form whose substitution instances are all valid arguments is called a validating argument form.

The point of view from which the following chapters are written may be expressed as follows. Validity is a structural characteristic of argument. Arguments are valid because of their form. Hence, the notions of valid argument and of validating argument form are correlative concepts. There can be no valid argument without a corresponding validating form. There can be no validating form without arguments which are validated by that form. Every valid argument is an instance of some validating form or other. Every validating argument form validates all of its substitution instances.

However, a specific argument is usually a substitution instance of many argument forms. The fact that one of its argument forms is non-validating does not authorize us to conclude that the argument is invalid. If an argument is valid, then it is validated by some validating form or other. Nevertheless, the fact that a specific argument form is nonvalidating does not imply that a substitution instance of that form is invalid.

For example, if "poet" means a writer of verse, then "Shakespeare was a poet. Therefore, he was a writer" is a valid argument. This argument is a substitution instance of the argument form, "*a* was a poet. Therefore, *a* was a writer." And this form is a validating form. But the argument is also a substitution instance of the form, "*A*. Therefore, *B*." This is obviously not a validating form.

We are now able to characterize the logic of conclusive argument by saying that it includes a study of the validating forms of argument. Logic is, therefore, called a formal study. Arguments are valid by virtue of their form. The argument form which validates an argument depicts all that we need to know about that argument in order to pronounce it valid.

The argument form, III above, contained statement variables, namely, the letters, "*A*" and "*B*". But we may also construct argument forms in which other sorts of variables occur. For example, the argument form

IV
IF A, THEN IT IS NOT THE CASE THAT ALL S IS P.
A
_____
SOME S IS NOT P.

is a case in which we find the occurrence not only of a statement variable but also of the term variables "S" and "P". These letters are used to designate terms. A substitution instance of this argument form is

V

IF JONES IS A LIAR, THEN IT IS NOT THE CASE THAT ALL MEN ARE TRUTHFUL.

JONES IS A LIAR.

SOME MEN ARE NOT TRUTHFUL.

In this case we have substituted the statement, "Jones is a liar" for "*A*", and we have substituted the terms "men" and "truthful" for the term variables "*S*" and "*P*".

Comparison of III and IV suggests the important distinction between elementary argument forms and non-elementary forms. An elementary argument form such as III is one in which statement variables but no other sorts of variables occur. Any other sort of argument form, e.g., IV, is a non-elementary form. Our plan is to study the validating forms of argument. Accordingly, we shall make a beginning by studying elementary validating forms. Then we shall go on to discuss non-elementary validating forms.

In order to represent the structure of an argument in such a way as to bring out the reason that it is valid, it is requisite that we represent the structure of the premisses and of the conclusion. We are, therefore, led to employ statement forms. Statement forms are not to be confused with statements. They are diagrams by which we represent any of an infinite variety of statements which are alike in respect to logical structure. Thus, "*A* or *B*" is such a diagram. Since it contains statement variables and no other sorts of variables, we call it an elementary statement form. We shall not attempt anything like an exhaustive classification of elementary statement forms, but a particular group of elementary forms of statement is especially important in the light of our purpose. To a consideration of these forms we now turn.

Proof

1

Elementary Validating Forms of Argument

The properties of being true and false are called truth values. We use the letters "T" and "F" as names designating the truth values, truth and falsity. We assume that every statement possesses just one truth value. Not every sentence is a statement. E.g., commands and questions are not statements and truth and falsity do not pertain to these sentences. No doubt, the assumption that every statement has just one truth value involves an element of idealization and simplification, insofar as it presupposes that everyday statements are definite in their meaning. In fact, we know that statements have a pronounced tendency to be vague. This is a complication which we shall find it expedient to ignore.

In many arguments, the vagueness of terms figuring therein is a logically irrelevant consideration. In such arguments, any admissible clarification of meaning would leave the question of validity or invalidity unaffected. However, other cases exist in which the validity of an argument hinges on a more precise interpretation of the meaning of its terms. We may avoid practical difficulties by restricting our attention to arguments in which the element of vagueness is without effect upon validity.

9

Hypothetical Statements

Statements of the form "If A then B" are familiar enough. Yet, though we may be said to understand such statements, we find it difficult to state their meaning in language which is clear. The difficulty may arise because of the fact that there are many meanings which can properly be conveyed by "if ... then". The circumstance that we can use the same linguistic form to communicate a variety of distinct meanings is apt to frustrate our first efforts at precise definition.

1. *Statements of logical implication*

Statements of the form "If A then B" are sometimes used to convey the sense which we could also express by a statement of the form "If A then necessarily B". This meaning of "if ... then" is closely connected with the notion of the validity of an argument. Instead of saying that an argument is valid, we can, without alteration of meaning, say that if its premises are true, then necessarily its conclusion is true.

In the statement form "If A then necessarily B", the variable "A" designates what is called the antecedent of the implication, whereas the variable "B" designates what is termed the consequent of the implication. Accordingly, a statement of the form "If A then necessarily B" is true just in case it is impossible that the antecedent is true and the consequent is false; or, equivalently, just in case the argument from its antecedent to its consequent is valid.

2. *Material implication statements*

The horseshoe symbol $\supset$ is used in place of "if ... then" in statements of material implication. "$A \supset B$" may be read "A horseshoe B", "If A then B", or "A only if B". In the statement form "$A \supset B$", the variable "A" designates the antecedent of the implication, and "B" designates the consequent of the implication. We may explain the meaning of a statement of material implication by specifying that such a statement is false just in case its antecedent is true and its consequent is false. Whereas the idea of necessity is involved in the meaning of a statement of logical implication, this idea is altogether irrelevant to the meaning expressed by statements of material implication.

It is useful to clarify the meaning of statements of material implication by referring to the table of truth values associated with the statement form "$A \supset B$".

A	$\supset$	B
T	T	T
T	F	F
F	T	T
F	T	F

Note that we have assigned truth values to the statements A and B in all possible ways. Each row in the truth table represents a definite assignment of truth values to the statements A and B. The truth values under the horseshoe compose the principal column of truth values. These are the values assigned to the total formula, $A \supset B$. The first row indicates that if T is assigned to A and B, it must also be assigned to $A \supset B$. The second row says that if T is assigned to A, and F is assigned to B, then F must be assigned to $A \supset B$. The third and fourth rows, jointly, tell us that if F is assigned to A, then T must be assigned to $A \supset B$, regardless of the truth value assigned to B. Each row tells us the truth value which must be assigned to the implication for any given distribution of truth values among the component sentences A and B.

A compound statement is said to be a truth function of its components just in case its truth value can be calculated, in truth-table fashion, from the truth values of its components, no matter what the distribution of truth values among those components may be. It is evident that statements of material implication are truth functional. And it is equally evident that statements of logical implication are not truth functional. To be sure, if the antecedent of a statement of logical implication is true and its consequent is false, the statement of logical implication must be false. But from any other distribution of truth values it would not be possible to infer whether the logical implication held. The distinction between truth functional and non-truth functional compound statements will later prove important.

We know, from the truth table of material implication, that a statement of material implication is true whenever either the antecedent is false or the consequent is true. To say that every proper use of "if . . . then" conforms to this requirement is out of the question. But that there is a proper use of the hypothetical form of statement which conforms to the truth table for material implication is not at all paradoxical, as the following considerations show.

Under what circumstances would the hypothetical statement "If Jones goes to China, Smith will remain in New York" be true? We may distinguish two cases: (a), the case in which it is true that Jones will go to China, and (b), the case in which it is false that he will go to China.

Case (a). In this case, the truth of the hypothetical statement depends entirely on whether Smith will remain in New York. If he does remain, the hypothetical statement is true. Otherwise, it is not. The statement did not say that there is a causal connection between Jones' going and Smith's remaining. The statement did not exclude the possibility that Smith's remaining might be a coincidence. No doubt, the speaker had his private reasons for making the statement, but these reasons are no part of what the hypothetical statement affirms. The statement is that if Jones goes, then as a matter of fact Smith will remain.

Case (b). In this case, since the antecedent is false, the speaker is not committed by his assertion to maintaining either that the consequent is true or that it is false. Hence, he cannot incur the charge of being in error, no matter whether Smith remains in New York or not. The statement does not say what would be the case if Jones did not go to China, but only what would be the case if he did. Since we assume that every statement must have just one truth value, and since the truth value of the hypothetical statement is not, in this case, falsity, it must be truth. Hence it is natural to interpret this hypothetical statement as a statement of material implication. Its truth conditions agree entirely with the truth table which we have just constructed.

Of course, we should not bother to affirm the truth, $A \supset B$, if we knew that A were false or that B were true. The reason for this is obvious. The utility of $A \supset B$ consists in its capacity to serve as a premiss in arguments such as

$A \supset B$ or $A \supset B$

A NOT-B

B NOT-A

If we knew that A was false, we could not use the truth of A as a premiss, and hence the left-hand argument would serve no purpose. The right-hand argument would also be useless, for it proves what is already known.

Similarly, if we knew the truth of B, we could not use the right-hand argument, which uses the falsity of B as a premiss. And we surely could not use the left-hand argument, for the conclusion, B, is already known.

Whenever it is at all important to affirm a statement of material implication, our reason is never that we know the falsity of the antecedent or the truth of the consequent. Then what could be a reason justifying the making of such hypothetical statements? It is past experience which justifies such statements, but the logic of such argument is a topic for Part 2.

Equivalence Statements

Corresponding to the two types of implication which we have discussed, there are two sorts of equivalence statements: logical equivalence statements and material equivalence statements.

LOGICAL EQUIVALENCE STATEMENTS

A logical equivalence statement has the form, "It is necessary that A if and only if B". In this statement form, the variables "A" and "B", depict what are termed the members of the equivalence statement. A logical equivalence statement is true just in case its members necessarily have the same truth value; such an equivalence statement is false just in case it is *possible* that its members have opposite truth values.

MATERIAL EQUIVALENCE STATEMENTS

A statement of the form "$A \equiv B$" we call a material equivalence statement. "$A \equiv B$" may be read "A if and only if *B*". The statements *A* and *B* which occur in $A \equiv B$ are termed the members of the equivalence. We may clarify the meaning of a material equivalence statement by remarking that such a statement is true just in case its members have the same truth value. This remark is the basis of the following truth table.

A	$\equiv$	B
T	T	T
T	F	F
F	F	T
F	T	F

Hence, a material equivalence statement is a truth function of its components. We note that whereas the idea of necessity enters into the meaning of a logical equivalence statement, it is altogether irrelevant to the meaning of a statement of material equivalence.

Denial

If *A* is a statement, $\sim A$ is the denial of *A*. Evidently, the truth value of $\sim A$ is opposite to that of *A* and the truth table for denial is

$\sim$	A
F	T
T	F

The principal column of truth values is written under the tilde. $\sim A$ may be read "It is false that *A*", or more simply, "not-*A*".

Alternation

A statement of the form "$A \vee B$" is called an alternation, the variables in the statement form depicting what are termed the alternatives of the alternation. An alternation is true just in case at least one of its alternatives is true, so we may read the wedge symbol **∨** as "or". The truth table for alternation, accordingly, is

A	$\lor$	B
T	T	T
T	T	F
F	T	T
F	F	F

There is another meaning of "or", the so-called exclusive meaning of "or", according to which the meaning of A or B is expressible by $\sim (A \equiv B)$.

Conjunction

$A \cdot B$ is said to be a conjunction, and A and B are called factors of the conjunction. The truth table of conjunction is

A	$\cdot$	B
T	T	T
T	F	F
F	F	T
F	F	F

The dot symbol for conjunction corresponds very closely to one use of "and" in ordinary language. But whereas "and" is used in ordinary language to couple nouns as well as sentences, the dot symbol is used only for the purpose of coupling sentences. Sometimes it is possible to analyze the noun-coupling use of "and" in terms of the sentence-coupling use which is expressed by the dot symbol. For example, "Brioni and Tobias are griffons" can be paraphrased by "Brioni is a griffon and Tobias is a griffon". However, some uses of "and" do not lend themselves thus to such simple paraphrase. For example, "Franz and Brioni are taking a walk together" cannot be rendered by "Franz is taking a walk together and so is Brioni".

Unless

The statement A unless B may usefully be construed as non-committal as to the truth value of A in the case of B's truth, and as affirming the truth of A in the case of B's falsity. Hence, A *unless* B means the same as $\sim B \supset A$. Now $\sim B \supset A$ is false just in case its antecedent is true and its consequent is false. This is to say that $\sim B \supset A$ is false just in case A and B are each false. But we know that the alternation $A \lor B$ is false just in case its alternatives are each false. Hence, A *unless* B may usefully be paraphrased by $A \lor B$.

Only if

A *only if* B may be construed as synonymous with $A \supset B$. The point may be illustrated thus:

THEODORA WILL BECOME A DOCTOR ONLY IF SHE IS PERMITTED TO STUDY MEDICINE.

Now this statement cannot properly be interpreted to mean that if she is permitted to study then she will automatically become a doctor. The clause following "only if" must be construed as the consequent of the implication. A, *if* B has B for its antecedent, but the insertion of "only" has the effect of interchanging the normal position of antecedent and consequent.

SUMMARY

Denials, conjunctions, alternations, material implications, and material equivalences are truth functions. The truth tables associated with these kinds of statement are conveniently remembered by the following rules:

1. The truth value of a denial is opposite to the truth value of the statement which is denied.

2. A conjunction is true just in case each factor is true.

3. An alternation is false just in case each alternative is false.

4. A material implication is false just in case its antecedent is true and its consequent is false.

5. A material equivalence is true just in case its members have the same truth value.

EXERCISES

1 Assuming that A and B are true statements and that C and D are false, evaluate the truth values of the following:

   a. $A \supset [(C \vee D) \supset B]$

   b. $C \equiv [D \vee (A \cdot C)]$

   c. $C \vee [D \equiv (A \cdot B)]$

   d. $(C \supset C) \supset C$

   e. $((C \supset C) \supset C) \supset C$

2 Assuming that A and B are true and that C is false, and assuming the truth of the following, evaluate, if possible, the truth value of D.

   a. $A \supset (B \supset D)$

   b. $A \supset (D \supset B)$

   c. $C \vee D$

   d. $(C \vee D) \supset C$

3 Assume that the following sentences are false, and that A is true, whereas B and C are false. Evaluate the truth value of D.

   a. $(B \supset D) \supset B$

   b. $(A \vee C) \equiv (A \supset D)$

   c. $\sim D \equiv (\sim D \cdot C)$

4 Express by means of the symbolism explained in the text:

   a. At most, one of (P, Q, R) is true.

   b. No statement in the set (P, Q) is true, unless at least one of (R, S) is true.

   c. Each statement in the set (P, Q) holds true only if R is true.

5 Translate the following sentences into the symbolism of logic.

   a. Unless the doctor comes, John will recover only if he has proper nursing.

   b. Since he has not come, we shall not hold the meeting.

   c. If he has not come, we shall not hold the meeting.

   d. Provided that we are all here, the meeting can begin.

   e. Either Jones left for China or he will be here if he has recovered sufficiently to attend.

Tautologies

If A is any statement, then $A \supset A$ is a statement whose truth table is

A	$\supset$	A
T	T	T
F	T	F

We constructed this table by assigning truth values to A in all possible ways. Since a material implication is falsified only in the TF case, i.e., only when its antecedent is true and its consequent false, and since this case does not occur in this truth table, the principal column must consist entirely of T's. A statement, the principal column of whose truth table consists entirely of T's, is called a tautology. The principal column of the truth table of a statement is the column of values assigned to that statement as a whole. In the truth table of an implication, the principal column occurs under $\supset$. In the case of an alternation, it occurs under **v**, etc.

A tautology is a necessary statement. It must be true no matter what distribution of truth values among its components occurs. Tautologies, therefore, may safely be counted among the laws of logic. We have a definite test procedure in the truth-table method whereby it can be certified whether or not a statement is a tautology.

Let us consider a different example. If A and B are any statements, then $A \supset (B \supset A)$ is a statement. The truth table for this sort of statement will have four rows. For there are two ways of assigning a truth value to A; for every way of assigning a truth value to A, there are two ways of assigning a truth value to B. Thus we have four distributions of truth values, namely,

A	B
T	T
T	F
F	T
F	F

Each of these four distributions, in view of the truth functional character of implication statements, permits us to calculate a truth value for the statement $A \supset (B \supset A)$. E.g., if

A and B are each true, the TT case, then $B \supset A$ will be true. Since an implication is true if its consequent is true, it follows that $A \supset (B \supset A)$ will also have truth for its truth value. The complete truth table is

A	$\supset$	$(B$	$\supset$	$A)$
T	T	T	T	T
T	T	F	T	T
F	T	T	F	F
F	T	F	T	F

The principal column of this truth table is the second column. Since it consists entirely of T's, $A \supset (B \supset A)$ must be a tautology.

One other very simple example may assist the reader.

A	$\mathbf{v}$	$\sim$	A
T	T	F	T
F	T	T	F

In the first row T is assigned to A. We then determine the truth value of $\sim A$. We know that A and $\sim A$ must have opposite truth values, so we assign F to $\sim A$. The alternatives joined by $\mathbf{v}$ are A and $\sim A$ whose truth values are T and F, respectively. Since an alternation with a true alternative must be true, we assign T to $A \mathbf{v} \sim A$. The calculation on the second row is similar.

That every substitution instance of $A \mathbf{v} \sim A$ is true may be called the Principle of Excluded Third. Since the assumption that every statement has just one truth value is built into our technique of truth-table construction, it is not surprising that the Principle of Excluded Third should turn up among the tautologies.

Let us now consider a statement form with three variables.

$[A$	$\supset$	$(B$	$\supset$	$C)]$	$\supset$	$[(A$	$\supset$	$B)$	$\supset$	$(A$	$\supset$	$C)]$
T	T	T	T	T		T	T		T	T	
T	T	F	T	T		T	F				
T	F	T	T	F		T	T				
T	F	F	T	F		T	F				
F	T	T	F	T		F	T				
F	T	F	F	T		F	F				
F	F	T	F	F		F	T				
F	F	F	F	F		F	F				

The eight possible distributions of truth values among the components are indicated so that it remains only to calculate the truth values which are to be inserted in the principal column. A little reflection will show that in the last four rows, where A is marked F, the total statement must be true; if A is false, $A \supset C$ must be true. But $A \supset C$ is the consequent of $(A \supset B) \supset (A \supset C)$. Since its consequent is true, $(A \supset B) \supset (A \supset C)$ must also be true. By parity of reasoning, the total statement must be true, since its consequent is true.

We know now that the second half of the principal column must consist entirely of T's. We have still to investigate the first four cases. In the first and third rows, C is marked true. Hence, in these rows T must occur in the principal column. For since C is marked true, so should $A \supset C$ be marked true. An implication with true consequent must be true. By parity of reasoning, since $A \supset C$ is marked T, we must assign T to the implication, $(A \supset B) \supset (A \supset C)$. And, by a further application of the same reasoning, we may conclude that the total statement must be marked true, since its consequent is now determined to be true.

We have only to reckon the truth values in the second and fourth rows, wherein A is marked true and C false.

$$[A \supset (B \supset C)] \supset [(A \supset B) \supset (A \supset C)]$$

T F	T F F	T	T T T F	T F F
T T	F T F	T	T F F T	T F F

Hence, the total statement must be a tautology.

EXERCISES

Verify that the following are tautological statement forms.

a. $[(A \supset B) \cdot (B \supset C)] \supset (A \supset C)$ (Transitivity)

b. $[(A \supset B) \cdot (C \supset \sim B)] \supset (C \supset \sim A)$ (The preclusion principle)

c. $(A \supset B) \equiv (\sim B \supset \sim A)$ (Transposition)

d. $A \equiv \sim \sim A$ (Double negation)

e. $(A \cdot B) \supset A$ (Simplification)

f. $A \supset (A \vee B)$ (Addition)

g. $(A \vee B) \equiv (\sim A \supset B)$ (Relation between alternation
    $(A \supset B) \equiv (\sim A \vee B)$ and implication)

h. $\sim (A \cdot B) \equiv (A \supset \sim B)$
    $\sim (A \cdot B) \equiv (\sim A \vee \sim B)$
    $\sim (A \supset B) \equiv (A \cdot \sim B)$
    $\sim (A \vee B) \equiv (\sim A \cdot \sim B)$ (Rules of denial)
    $\sim (A \equiv B) \equiv (A \equiv \sim B)$
    $\sim (A \equiv B) \equiv (\sim A \equiv B)$

i. $[A \cdot (A \supset B)] \supset B$ (Modus ponens)

j. $[\sim B \cdot (A \supset B)] \supset \sim A$ (Modus tollens)

k. $A \vee \sim A$ (Principle of excluded third)

l. $\sim (A \cdot \sim A)$ (Principle of contradiction)

m. $[\sim A \cdot (A \vee B)] \supset B$ (Principle of denying
                                            an alternative)

The Fundamental Principle

The antecedent of a tautological implication may be described
as tautologically implying the consequent. "The leading principle of an argument" means a material implication whose consequent is the conclusion of the argument and whose antecedent
is the conjunction of the premisses of the argument. Then our
fundamental principle may be formulated in either of the following ways (which are equivalent):

1. If the conjunction of premisses of an argument tautologically implies the conclusion, then the argument is valid.
2. If the leading principle of an argument is a tautology, then
   the argument is valid. In other words, if the statement
   $(A_1 \cdot A_2 \cdots \cdot A_j) \supset B$ is tautological, then the argument

$$A_1$$
$$\cdot$$
$$\cdot$$
$$\cdot$$
$$\frac{A_j}{B}$$

is valid. It must be noted that the fundamental principle
states a sufficient but not a necessary condition for validity.

EXERCISES

1   Show that the following are validating forms of argument.

a. $A \lor B$
     $\sim B$
     ─────
     A

b. $A \supset B$
     $\sim B$
     ─────
     A

c. $A \supset B$
     A
     ─────
     B

d. A
     B
     ─────
     $A \cdot B$

e. $A \supset [\sim B \lor (C \supset \sim B)]$
     B
     ──────────────────────
     $A \supset \sim C$

2   a.   Show that a tautology may validly be concluded from any set of premisses.

    b.   Show that any conclusion may validly be inferred from a statement of the form $\sim (A \supset A)$.

3   Show that the following argument form is a validating form.

$A \supset B$
$B \supset C$
$A \supset \sim C$
─────
$\sim A$

4   We have two marbles, X and Y; two cards, P and Q; and a box.

Assume: Either X or Y is in the box.
          At most one of the cards is in the box.
          If X is in the box, so is P.
          If Y is in the box, so is Q.

Prove: Either P or Q is in the box.
          At most one of the marbles is in the box.
          If P is in the box, so is X.
          If Q is in the box, so is Y.

The Oblique Method

It is a tedious matter to construct truth tables for statement forms which contain many components. The following indirect method is often useful.

Consider a statement of the form

$$(A \supset B) \supset [(B \supset C) \supset (A \supset C)]$$

Suppose, for the sake of argument, that an F occurs in some row, in the principal column. We obtain as our first step

(1) $\qquad (A \supset B) \supset [(B \supset C) \supset (A \supset C)]$
$\qquad\qquad\qquad$ F

Since the assignment of F to an implication signifies a TF case, we have

(2) $\qquad (A \supset B) \supset [(B \supset C) \supset (A \supset C)]$
$\qquad\qquad$ T $\quad$ F $\qquad\quad$ F

The same reasoning leads to

(3) $\qquad (A \supset B) \supset [(B \supset C) \supset (A \supset C)]$
$\qquad\qquad$ T $\quad$ F $\quad$ T $\quad$ F $\quad$ F

And by exactly the same reasoning we obtain

(4) $\qquad (A \supset B) \supset [(B \supset C) \supset (A \supset C)]$
$\qquad\qquad$ T $\quad$ F $\quad$ T $\quad$ F $\quad$ TFF

The same statement must receive the same truth value on the same row of a truth table. So we have

(5) $\qquad (A \supset B) \supset [(B \supset C) \supset (A \supset C)]$
$\qquad\qquad$ T T $\quad$ F $\quad$ T F $\;$ F $\;$ T F F

But now we cannot consistently assign a truth value to B. If we mark B true, then $B \supset C$ is marked true, despite the fact that it has a true antecedent and a false consequent. If we mark B false, $A \supset B$ would be marked true, although its antecedent is true and its consequent is false.

It follows that the initial assumption of an F in the principal column involves an inconsistent assignment of truth values to the components. Hence, the statement must be a tautology. There can be no F in the principal column of its truth table.

It is convenient to arrange the work in the following manner:

$\qquad (A \supset B) \supset [(B \supset C) \supset (A \supset C)]$

T	F			F		
			T		F	
T			F		T	F
T T ?	F	?	T F	F	T	F F

The double line announces that the next line summarizes the preceding three lines. The question marks signify the locus of the contradiction.

EXERCISES

1   Discuss the validity of arguments of the following forms:

$(A \supset \sim B) \supset [G \supset (B \vee C)]$

$\sim A$

$\sim C$

$\sim G \vee B$

2   THERE ARE THREE SUSPECTS (X, Y, Z) AND THREE WITNESSES (P, Q, R). AT LEAST ONE OF THE SUSPECTS (X, Y, Z) IS GUILTY. IF P TOLD THE TRUTH, THEN SO DID THE OTHER WITNESSES. IF Y IS GUILTY, THEN Q LIED. IF Z IS GUILTY, THEN R LIED.

IF P TOLD THE TRUTH, X WAS GUILTY.

Omniparence

A tautological statement is one whose truth table's principal column is an unbroken column of T's. We may also call a statement form tautological in the related sense that all of its substitution instances are tautological.

On the other hand, we shall call the statement A omniparent if and only if its truth table contains, for its principal column, an unbroken column of F's. "Tautological" and "omniparent" are terms referring to truth table procedure. We verify the application of these terms by a truth table construction.

To save writing, it is sometimes possible to ascertain that a statement is omniparent by the oblique method. In other words, we assume the truth of the statement and then show that out of this assumption an inconsistent truth value assignment results. E.g.,

$$\sim (A \vee \sim A)$$
$$\text{T} \quad \text{F} \quad \text{F} \quad \text{F} \quad \text{T}$$

Hence, $\sim (A \vee \sim A)$ has the truth value F, no matter what the truth value of A.

A statement may be *inconsistent* even though it is not omnip-arent. This fact may be brought out by an example. The con-junction, "(Every whale is a mammal · No fish is a mammal) · Some whales are fishes", is evidently an inconsistent statement. The truth value T *could* not consistently be assigned to the fac-tors of this conjunction. Nevertheless, it must be noted that the rules of truth-value assignment do not of themselves rule out the possibility that this conjunction is true. The *elementary* state-ment form of this conjunction is $(A \cdot B) \cdot C$, which is a non-omniparent form. This form does not display those logical features of the factors of the conjunction which make that par-ticular conjunction inconsistent. Every omniparent statement is inconsistent, but not every inconsistent statement is omniparent. And, by the same token, every tautology is necessarily true, but not every necessary truth is a tautology.

To explain what we mean by "inconsistency", we must first explain the idea of a derivation.

A derivation of the statement A from the set of premisses, α, is a sequence of valid arguments, $(a_1, a_2, \ldots, a_j)$, such that a_j has for its conclusion the statement A and such that every premiss of every argument in the sequence is either

1. a member of α;

2. a conclusion of some earlier argument in the sequence.

Although we provide no universal criterion for validity, we remark that every *rigorous* derivation is associated with an annotation which specifies how the arguments in the derivation may be validated.

We shall assume that there exists a derivation of the conclu-sion of an argument from its premisses if and only if the argu-ment is valid. Now, an inconsistent statement (or set of state-ments) is one from which an omniparent statement is *derivable*. In other words, if there exists a derivation of an omniparent statement from a set of statements, α, then and only then is that set of statements inconsistent. A statement may not be omnipa-rent and yet may well be inconsistent in the present sense. For example, "Balzac was a novelist but not a writer" is inconsistent and yet non-omniparent. From this statement we can derive the omniparent statement, "Balzac was a writer · Balzac was not a writer".

Validation by Derivation

Instead of validating an elementary form of argument by a single step according to the Fundamental Principle, it is often more convenient to construct a derivation of the conclusion from the premisses. The individual arguments which make up the derivation are validated by the fundamental principle and by an appropriate truth-table analysis. The point is that by this procedure we avoid unconscionably complicated truth tables.

The following argument forms are used repeatedly in our derivations. That they are validating forms of argument may be shown by the fundamental principle.

A

$\dfrac{A \supset B}{B}$ (The method of affirming the antecedent)

$\sim B$

$\dfrac{A \supset B}{\sim A}$ (The method of denying the consequent)

$A \lor B$

$\dfrac{\sim A}{B}$ (The method of denying an alternative)

A

$\dfrac{B}{A \cdot B}$ (The method of conjunction)

On pages 20–21, we listed and named a number of tautological statement forms: transitivity, preclusion, addition, simplification, double negation, the principles of excluded third and contradiction, the relation between alternation and implication, and the rules for denial. If the student learns to recognize these tautological forms, he will be materially assisted in acquiring facility in proof construction.

Consider an argument of the form:

I

(1) $A \supset (B \lor C)$

(2) $\sim B$

(3) $C \supset B$

(4) $\dfrac{A}{B \cdot \sim B}$

Our first step is to advance by the method of affirming the antecedent from (1) and (4) to

(5) $B \vee C$

Using (2) and (5) and the method of denying an alternative, we obtain

(6) C

Now we use (3) and (6) and the method of affirming the antecedent to obtain

(7) B

From (2) and (7), using the rule of conjunction, we finally obtain

$$B \cdot \sim B$$

We have, in effect, shown how to construct a derivation of $B \cdot \sim B$ from the premisses (1)–(4), no matter what the statements A, B, and C might be. It follows that I is a validating argument form. It also follows that the premisses of any substitution instance of I must be an inconsistent set of statements.

The Counterset of an Argument

The counterset of an argument H (also called the C-set of H), is the set of H's premisses augmented by the denial of H's conclusion. The C-set of the argument

$A \supset B$
A
___
B

is the set $[A \supset B, A, \sim B]$. We see at once, not only in this case but universally, that if H is a valid argument then and only then is its C-set inconsistent. This follows directly from the meaning of "validity". An argument is valid just in case it would be inconsistent for its premisses to be true and its conclusion false. But this says the same as that an argument is valid if and only if its C-set is inconsistent. We may, therefore, prove an argument valid by deriving an omniparent sentence from its

C-set. But we must keep in mind that mere failure to prove inconsistency does not itself prove that there is none to be derived. Mere failure to establish validity does not suffice to prove invalidity.

To illustrate the use of the concept of C-set, take the argument

$A \supset (B \vee C)$
$\sim B$
$C \supset B$
_____
$\sim A$

The counterset of this argument is $[A \supset (B \vee C),\ \sim B,$ $C \supset B,\ \sim \sim A]$. From $\sim \sim A$, by the rule of double negation, we obtain A. Then by the reasoning we used in argument I above, we advance to $B \cdot \sim B$. Hence the C-set is inconsistent and, consequently, the original argument must be valid.

EXERCISES

1 Show that an argument is valid, if its premisses compose an inconsistent set.

2 Show that a logically necessary premiss is redundant.

3 Show that the argument

$$A_1$$
$$\cdot$$
$$\cdot$$
$$\cdot$$
$$\dfrac{A_{j+1}}{B}$$

is valid if and only if

$$A_1$$
$$\cdot$$
$$\cdot$$
$$\dfrac{A_j}{A_{j+1} \supset B}$$

is valid,

4   Prove that the following sets of statements are inconsistent:

  a. $A \supset \sim C$
     $(B \vee A) \supset (C \vee B)$
     $\sim B$
     A

  b. $R \supset C$
     $W \supset S$
     $O \supset \sim C$
     $O \supset \sim S$
     $F \vee (R \vee W)$
     $O \cdot \sim F$

The Principle of Truth Functionality

We have noted before that a truth functional statement is one whose truth value can under all circumstances be unambiguously calculated, in truth-table fashion, from the truth values assigned to its components. It is useful to employ a notation which suggests this truth functional dependence of certain statements upon certain of its components. Let f_B be an elementary truth functional statement form in which the variable "B" occurs. By "the result of applying f_B to the statement A", we mean the result of substituting A for all occurrences of "B" in f_B. We symbolize the result of this substitution by the symbol "$f_B(A)$". For example, f_B might be the statement form, "$B \vee$ Jones is guilty". A might be the statement, "Jones is innocent". Then $f_B(A)$ would be the statement, "Jones is innocent $\vee$ Jones is guilty". We emphasize that we use f-symbols only to designate truth functional statements or statement forms.

Truth functional statements have a characteristic which is of the utmost logical importance and which we may express by stating that

II $\qquad\qquad A \equiv B \supset [f_c(A) \equiv f_c(B)]$

is tautological, whatever the statements A and B may be. This is the principle of truth functionality. To certify that II is a tautology, let us investigate the consequences of placing an F in the principal column of the truth table of II. If there were a way of assigning truth values to A and B so as to falsify II, then in that truth-value assignment A and B would have to receive the same truth value, whereas $f_c(A)$ and $f_c(B)$ would have to receive opposite truth values. But this is impossible, for it disagrees with our condition that $f_c(A)$ and $f_c(B)$ are truth functional. To see this more clearly, let $a_1, \ldots, a_i$ be the entire list of atomic statements in f_c. For any assignment of truth values to $a_1, \ldots, a_i$ and for any truth value of A, the truth value of $f_c(A)$ will be uniquely determined. This follows from the truth functionality of f_c. For the same truth values assigned to $a_1, \ldots, a_i$ if the same truth value is assigned to B as is assigned to A, $f_c(B)$ must receive the same truth value as $f_c(A)$. Hence, it is impossible to assign the same truth value to A and B while opposite truth values are assigned to $f_c(A)$ and $f_c(B)$.

We may illustrate the principle of truth functionality by an example. Take f_c to be $\sim C$. Then II becomes

III $\qquad\qquad (A \equiv B) \supset [\sim A \equiv \sim B]$

which is obviously tautological.

Rules of Deletion

It follows from the principle of truth functionality that the argument

A

$f_c(A \supset B)$

$\overline{f_c(B)}$

is valid. To demonstrate that it is, we shall derive $f_c(B)$ from the class of premisses, $[A, f_c(A \supset B)]$. We begin by verifying that

$$A \supset [(A \supset B) \equiv B]$$

is a tautology. Then by the Fundamental Principle we derive from the premiss A

(1) $\qquad\qquad (A \supset B) \equiv B$

Using the Fundamental Principle and the Principle of Truth Functionality, we obtain from (1)

(2) $\qquad\qquad f_c(A \supset B) \equiv f_c(B)$

Using the preceding line and the premiss $f_c(A \supset B)$ and the Fundamental Principle, we obtain our conclusion, $f_c(B)$.

One can think of this conclusion as obtained from the premisses by deleting $A \supset$ in $f_c(A \supset B)$. It will be noted that the method of affirming the antecedent is a special case of the validating argument form which has just been established. If f_c is identical with the variable C, then $f_c(A \supset B)$ is the same as $A \supset B$, and the conclusion $f_c(B)$ is B.

To illustrate the method of argument which has just been validated, we may, from the premisses A and $B \lor (A \supset C)$, infer $B \lor C$. We simply delete $A \supset$ from $B \lor (A \supset C)$ and infer what survives the deletion. We shall call this method of argument "deleting the antecedent".

It may likewise be established that

$$A$$
$$\frac{f_c(A \cdot B)}{f_c(B)}$$

is valid. From the first premiss and the Fundamental Principle we obtain

(1) $(A \cdot B) \equiv B$

From (1), the Principle of Truth Functionality, and the Fundamental Principle, we have

(2) $f_c(A \cdot B) \equiv f_c(B)$

Using the second premiss and (2) and the Fundamental Principle, we have

$$f_c(B)$$

We may interpret this method of argument as deletion of a factor of a conjunction. The following is an example of its use. From A and $B \supset [(A \cdot C) \lor D]$, we may infer $B \supset (C \lor D)$. We simply delete $A \cdot$ from the second premiss and infer what survives the deletion to obtain our conclusion. We call this method of argument "deleting a factor". It is obvious that either factor of a conjunction may be deleted, provided that it is asserted in a premiss.

The rule of deleting an alternative is also derivable. But, as might be expected, the alternative to be deleted must be denied in a premiss. That is, the following argument is valid.

$\sim A$

$f_c(A \lor B)$

$f_c(B)$

The argument follows the preceding pattern almost exactly. We first establish out of the premisses that

$$(A \lor B) \equiv B$$

The remainder of the argument is as in the preceding cases.

To illustrate the use of the preceding rules, we may ask what can properly be inferred from

(1) $\sim A$

(2) $B \supset [A \lor (C \supset D)]$

(3) C

From the first two premisses, by deleting an alternative, we obtain

(4) $B \supset (C \supset D)$

By deleting the antecedent and using (3) and (4), we obtain

(5) $B \supset D$

It can also be established that the argument

A

$f_c(A \equiv B)$

$f_c(B)$

is valid. The justification is left to the reader. We call this method of argument "deleting a member of an equivalence". To illustrate its use, we may consider what we may infer from the premisses

$$\sim B$$

$$A \supset (B \lor C)$$

$$D \supset (\sim B \equiv \sim C)$$

From the first two premisses, by deleting an alternative, we obtain

$$A \supset C$$

Using the first and third premisses, by deleting a member of the equivalence, we obtain

$$D \supset \sim C$$

The last two lines, by the Preclusion Principle, give us

$$D \supset \sim A$$

SUMMARY

In truth functional contexts we may delete a factor of a conjunction, the antecedent of an implication, or a member of an equivalence, provided that the statement deleted is a premiss of the argument; we may delete an alternative, provided that its denial is a premiss of the argument. These rules of deletion are useful in establishing validity in the case of many arguments whose validating forms are elementary. It is, of course, true that for these cases the truth-table method suffices. But the truth-table procedure is often tedious.

EXERCISES

1   If Jones lied, then either he lost his nerve and was guilty or he tried to protect someone else. He did lose his nerve, but he didn't try to protect someone else. If Smith told the truth, then Jones was not guilty. Therefore, Smith told the truth only if Jones did not lie.

2   Jones will be found guilty unless the judge makes a surprising ruling or the attorney for the defense discovers new evidence. The judge will not make a surprising ruling. Therefore, Jones will be found guilty unless the attorney for the defense discovers new evidence.

3   If Bacon authored Shakespeare's plays, then either De Vere composed the sonnets or Bacon did not write the *Essays*. If Miss Bacon of Boston is correct, Bacon is the author of the plays. If De Vere composed the sonnets, Miss Bacon of Boston is not correct.

Therefore, if Miss Bacon is correct, Bacon did not author the *Essays*.

4 If S is the father of R, then C must be the cousin of R. If A is the mother of R, B must be the niece of S. If C is the cousin of R, then B cannot be the niece of S. If A is not the mother of R, then Q is not the son of S. Therefore, S is not the father of R unless Q is the son of S.

5 If we are given the six statements (P, Q, X, Y, A, B), satisfying the following conditions:

  a. At least one of the statements (P, Q) is true

  b. At most one of the statements (X, Y) is true

  c. Just one of the statements (A, B) is true

  d. $P \supset A$
      $Q \supset A$
      $\sim Y \supset B$

what must the truth value of X be?

6 If we are given the six statements (P, Q, X, Y, A, B), satisfying the following conditions:

  a. At least one of the statements (P, Q) is true

  b. At most one of the statements (X, Y) is true

  c. Just one of the statements (A, B) is true

  d. $A \supset \sim Q$
      $\sim Y \supset Y$
      $B \supset X$

what is the truth value of Q?

7 If Jones lied, then he was guilty. If Smith spoke the truth, then he was innocent. But either Jones was innocent or Smith was guilty. Therefore, either Jones did not lie or Smith did not speak the truth.

8 If I tell the truth, I shall be punished. If I lie, I shall despise myself. Since I must either lie or tell the truth, I shall either be punished or I shall despise myself.

9 If Moby Dick was a mammal, he was a whale. He wasn't a mammal. Therefore, he wasn't a whale.

   Does this argument have an elementary validating form? If not, on what does its validity depend?

10 IF JONES EXERCISES NORMALLY AND DIETS, HE MUST LOSE WEIGHT. BUT HE DOES DIET.

   HENCE, IF HE EXERCISES NORMALLY, HE MUST LOSE WEIGHT.

11 JOHNSON COMMITTED THE BURGLARY UNLESS FRANKLIN LIED.

IF THE WATCHMAN WASN'T THERE, FRANKLIN DID NOT LIE.

IF THE WATCHMAN WAS THERE, THE SAFE WAS LOCKED.

IF THE SAFE WAS LOCKED, THE WATCHMAN WASN'T THERE.

JOHNSON COMMITTED THE BURGLARY.

12 EITHER, IF HE LEFT TOWN, HE IS IN HIDING, OR ELSE IT MUST BE THAT
IF HE LEFT TOWN, HE IS ON HIS WAY TO VISIT JUMBA.

HE LEFT TOWN, BUT HE IS NOT IN HIDING.

SO HE IS ON HIS WAY TO VISIT JUMBA.

13 EITHER JONES LIED OR HE IS GUILTY.

IF JONES LIED, THEN HE IS GUILTY.

JONES IS GUILTY.

14 IF BERKELEY IS RIGHT, WE PERCEIVE OBJECTS.

IF ALL THAT WE PERCEIVE ARE SENSATIONS, THEN WE DO NOT PERCEIVE
OBJECTS.

IF ALL THAT WE PERCEIVE ARE SENSATIONS, BERKELEY ISN'T RIGHT.

15 IF SLIVRIENSKY MOVES HIS PAWN, IT WILL BE CAPTURED.

IF HIS PAWN IS CAPTURED, IT IS CHECKMATE AS A MATTER OF COURSE.

NOW EITHER HE MUST RESIGN OR MOVE HIS PAWN, OR IT IS CHECKMATE
AS A MATTER OF COURSE.

SLIVRIENSKY *never* RESIGNS.

HE WILL BE CHECKMATED AS A MATTER OF COURSE.

16 EITHER THE KEY FITS, OR IF IT IS GOLD IT IS AN ORNAMENT.

IT IS GOLD.

EITHER IT ISN'T GOLD, OR IF IT FITS IT IS AN ORNAMENT.

THE KEY IS AN ORNAMENT.

17 Assume:

a. At most two of the propositions (P, Q, R) are true

b. At least two of the propositions (X, Y, Z) are true

c. If X then P
If Y then Q
If Z then R.

Then prove:

a. At most two of the propositions (X, Y, Z) are true

b. At least two of the propositions (P, Q, R) are true

c. If P then X
If Q then Y
If R then Z.

2

Non-elementary
Validating Forms
of Argument

In the preceding chapter, the validity of arguments has been investigated by the help of elementary statement and argument forms. Up to now, we have represented the structure of an argument by considering how atomic sentences may be combined to form compound sentences and how atomic and compound sentences may be combined to form valid arguments. However, in representing the structure of such arguments we did not need to disclose the structure of the atomic units entering into the arguments. It is characteristic of the logic of elementary validating forms that it systematically ignores the structure of atomic sentences. In that mode of analysis, the atomic sentences in an argument were represented by statement variables. But now we shall discuss how the internal complexity of atomic sentences may be relevant to the validity of the arguments in which they figure. In such discussion we shall utilize non-elementary statement forms containing term variables and other devices for depicting the internal structure of atomic sentences.

We shall commence our discussion by restricting our consideration to certain forms of statement which are, somewhat inexactly, called subject-predicate forms. Subsequently, we shall remove this unnecessary restriction and consider other forms of statement as well. The advantage of this procedure is

36

the advantage of beginning with the simple before dealing with the complex.

Subject-predicate statements are of two kinds: singular and general.

Singular Statements

Statements of the form "*a* is an *S*", or "*a* is not an *S*" are singular in form. Statements of the first form are singular affirmative. Those of the second sort are said to be singular negative. In the diagram "*a* is an *S*", "*a*" denotes the subject term of the statement and "*P*" denotes the predicate term of the sentence. The subject term of a singular statement is to be construed as referring to some specific item in the universe of discourse and the predicate is to be construed as designating a property or feature which can significantly be ascribed to the item named by the subject term. Thus, "John is wretched" is a substitution instance of "*a* is *P*", but "John is a prime number" is not, since this form of words is not significant.

To clarify the sense of the expression, "singular statement", we may raise the question: is the fictional sentence, "Mr. Pickwick is bald", a singular sentence? The answer is in the negative. For no entity corresponds to the expression "Mr. Pickwick". The analysis of fictional sentences is a problem which, fortunately, we can evade without adversely affecting any discussion which we propose to enter upon.

General Statements of Subject-Predicate Form

The use of the word "general" in subject-predicate logic refers to the presence of "all", "some", and "no", or synonyms of these, as they occur in the statement forms:

A   All *S* is *P*

E   No *S* is *P*

I   Some *S* is *P*

O   Some *S* is not *P*

In these forms, "*S*" and "*P*" are said to designate the subject and predicate terms, respectively. The letters "A", "E", "I", and "O" are traditionally employed to designate the statement forms with which they are associated in the above enumeration. A and E are said to be universal statements. I and O are called particular statements. Again, A and I are said to be affirmative, whereas E and O are called negative statements. It is useful to employ the abbreviations, A(*SP*), E(*SP*), I(*SP*) and O(*SP*) respectively, in place of

All *S* is *P*,   an A statement with subject *S* and predicate *P*
No *S* is *P*,   an E statement with subject *S* and predicate *P*
Some *S* is *P*,   an I statement with subject *S* and predicate *P*
Some *S* is not *P*, an O statement with subject *S*, and predicate *P*

By the quantity of a general statement is meant that the statement is either universal or particular. By its quality is meant that it is either affirmative or negative.

The following table summarizes the preceding remarks:

Statement form	Abbreviation	Quality	Quantity
All *S* is *P*	A(*SP*)	Affirmative	Universal
No *S* is *P*	E(*SP*)	Negative	Universal
Some *S* is *P*	I(*SP*)	Affirmative	Particular
Some *S* is not *P*	O(*SP*)	Negative	Particular

The preceding classification of subject-predicate forms into four types of general statements and two types of singular statements seems clear enough when stated abstractly. But how shall specific statements be classified according to this scheme? We encounter no problem when we consider "Socrates is wise" or "All men are mortal". But how shall we classify "Bess murdered all of her children"? One answer which, indeed, has merit is to say that this statement has no place in the subject-predicate classification. It is true that this statement is a substitution instance of the statement form, "*a* is in the relation *R* to all *P*'s". It is true, again, that this form is not one of the enumerated subject-predicate forms of statement. But we need not be satisfied to leave the matter thus. In the first place, the circumstance that a statement has a certain form does not mean that this form is its only form. In the second place, if we can construe this statement as being of subject-predicate form, then there are many arguments in which it occurs whose validity can be tested according to a very simple technique. Hence, we may be strongly tempted to assimilate this statement to one of the subject-predicate forms in order to apply the rules of subject-predicate logic to it. Subject-predicate logic is, as we have said, very simple, and this simplicity is a considerable inducement for tolerating a somewhat unnatural subject-predicate interpretation of statements even when they are so evidently relational in structure as "Bess murdered all of her children". Thus, we may interpret this statement to mean the same as "Bess has the property of having murdered all of her children" or the same as "All of Bess's children had the property of being murdered by Bess" or "Murdering is a relation in which Bess stood to each of her children". Such constructions are forced, but they are not erroneous, and sometimes they permit application of the extremely simplified methods of reasoning which we shall proceed now to explain.

Venn Diagrams

Let us take some non-empty system of objects which we call a universe of discourse, and represent it by a rectangle. If we inscribe two intersecting circles in it and regard these circles as representing two classes m and n, then in effect we have divided our universe into four exclusive sets:

I, or the things in m but not in n
II, or the intersection of m and n, the things common to m and n
III, or the things not in m but in n
IV, or the things neither in m nor in n

Figure 1 is to be interpreted as follows: we are to assume that at least one object falls within the universe of discourse so that not all four of the sets I, II, III, IV are empty. But the diagram does not inform us, as it stands, which of the sets has elements within it. We now adopt the following conventions:

1. To represent that a set is empty, we shade the area representing that set. E.g., Figure 2 represents that the set II is empty.

2. If an area is unshaded, then the diagram must be considered to signify neither that the class represented by the area is empty nor that it is non-empty. In such a case, the question is left open; the diagram is non-committal on the point. Thus, in Figure 2, the diagram expresses no judgment as to whether the set I is empty.

3. To represent the existence of an object in the class represented by a particular area, we place an asterisk in that area. For example, in Figure 3 we signify the presence of at least one object in class III.

4. The location of an asterisk on the rim of a circle indicates that no judgment is being rendered that objects exist on one side of the line nor, again, that objects exist on the other side of the line. For example, Figure 4 represents the presence of objects in *m* but leaves undecided whether such objects are in I.

We may now interpret A, E, I, and O statements by the use of Venn diagrams.

Let the circle S in Figure 5 represent the set of things to which

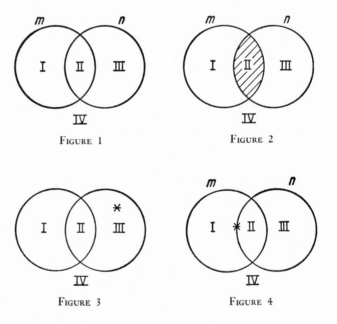

FIGURE 1   FIGURE 2

FIGURE 3   FIGURE 4

S applies and let the circle P be the set of things to which *P* applies. Then the statement *All* S *is* P may be construed as signifying that the set I is empty. Hence, A(*SP*) corresponds to the instruction to shade the area in S and outside P. In other words, *All* S *is* P says that if there is something in S, it must also be in P.

In Figure 6 we interpret the statement *No* S *is* P as instructing us to shade the intersection of the two circles. Hence, E(*SP*) signifies that the set II is an empty set. In other words, it signifies that if anything is in S then it is not in P.

I and O statements are represented by placing asterisks in the appropriate areas. Thus:

I(*SP*) in Figure 7 instructs us that at least one object occurs in the intersection of S and P. O(*SP*) in Figure 8 instructs us to place an asterisk in the area outside P and inside S.

By drawing three intersecting circles, we divide the universe of discourse into eight exclusive sets (Figure 9).

By shading or placing asterisks in the appropriate areas, it is possible to represent the meaning of a conjunction of general statements in which three classes are mentioned. For example,

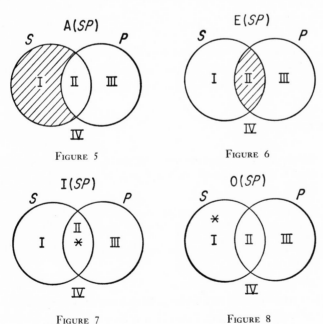

FIGURE 5

FIGURE 6

FIGURE 7

FIGURE 8

the statement *No* S *is* P *and every* Q *is* P may be represented by Figure 10, where the sets I, II, and III are the sets to which the predicates S, Q, and P apply, respectively.

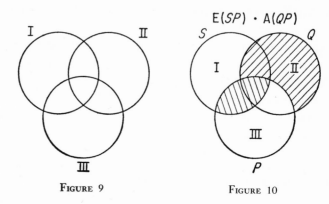

FIGURE 9   FIGURE 10

It will be noted that Figure 10 permits us to verify that any argument is valid if it is of the form

NO S IS P

EVERY Q IS P

NO S IS Q

By performing the operations which the premisses of the argument instruct us to perform, we have necessarily performed the operation by which the conclusion is represented.

EXERCISES

1   Explain by Venn diagrams why *All* S *is* P must be equivalent to *No* S *is non*-P, and why *No* S *is* P must be equivalent to *All* S *is non*-P.

2   Use Venn diagrams to illustrate your explanation why it is illegitimate to infer *All* P *is* S from *All* S *is* P.

3   Use Venn diagrams in discussing the validity of the following arguments:

  a.   EVERY GHOST WEARS CHAINS.

       WHOEVER HAS LIVED A THOUSAND YEARS MUST BE A GHOST.

       WHOEVER HAS LIVED A THOUSAND YEARS WEARS CHAINS.

b. NO CAT BARKS.

SOME CATS SPIT.
_____
SOME WHO SPIT DO NOT BARK.

c. WHO STEALS MY PURSE STEALS TRASH.

PICKPOCKETS DON'T STEAL TRASH.
_____
MY PURSE IS SAFE FROM PICKPOCKETS.

4 By the use of two Venn diagrams, discuss the validity of the following:

ONLY HUMANS CAN LAUGH.

SOME WHO LAUGH ARE WITLESS.

NO BIRD IS HUMAN.
_____
SOME WITLESS BEINGS ARE NOT BIRDS.

The Meaning of A and E Statements

A and E statements are hypothetical in import. The statement *All* S *is* P expresses what we could also say by the statement, *If anything is an* S, *it is a* P. Such hypothetical statements are sometimes used to express logical or causal connections, but we shall interpret them as *generalized statements of material implication.* Our reasons are closely related to those given in connection with our decision to regard conditional statements as material implication statements. The meaning of A(*SP*) is then expressed by the statement

(1) $(x)(x \text{ is an } S \supset x \text{ is a } P)$

which we may read, "For any x, if x is an S then x is a P". For example, "All dogs bark" may be regarded as equivalent to

(2) $(x)(x \text{ is a dog} \supset x \text{ barks})$

which may be read, "For any x, if x is a dog then x barks".

It should be noted that (1) is a statement form containing the syntactical variables "S" and "P". It is a symbolic device for representing statements. However, (2) is not a diagram of a statement, but one of the statements represented by the diagram, (1). Furthermore, we find in (2) the occurrence of a variable, "x", used to express generality. We have made use of syntactical variables all along, but here we are explicitly using variables in statements which are employed to describe not words, but things.

Whereas we may explain the meaning of the word "dog" by saying that it signifies the property of being a dog and that whatever it applies to is a dog, we explain the meaning of the variable "x" by associating it with a range of values. The statement (2) above may be explained now in the following manner. The statement "$(x)(x$ is a dog $\supset x$ barks)" is true just in case each object in the range of the variable "x" satisfies the condition, "x is a dog $\supset x$ barks". It is of no importance to us now what the range of values of "x" is. It is natural to take as the range of "x" the class of objects making up the space-time order of nature. However, any well-defined and non-empty set of objects may be specified as the range of "x". In the absence of a range assignment to the variable "x", (2) would not be a statement, and the condition for assigning it a truth value would not be specified. We call "x" an individual variable. Other individual variables employed in this book are

$$u, v, w, y, z$$

with or without numerical subscripts.

The symbol "$(x)(\ \ )$" is called a *universal quantifier*. The formula, which may or may not contain "x", and which is enclosed in the parentheses of the quantifier, is called the *scope* of the quantifier. The scope of a quantifier is always so designated by the parentheses enclosing it which follow immediately after the symbol "(x)". The variable, which occurs in the quantification prefix, is called the variable of quantification. In the ordinary case, the scope of a quantifier contains occurrences of the variable of quantification. But the exceptional case must be interpreted also. We adopt the convention that if A is a complete statement then $(x)(A)$ is to mean the same as A. E.g., (x) (Jones is happy) means the same as "Jones is happy".

In the statement $(x)(x$ is $S \supset x$ is $P)$ the occurrences of "x" in the scope refer back to the quantifier. In this sentence we say that the occurrences of the variable in the scope are bound by the quantifier. But a more complex case can arise. Consider the statement *If anything is S then everything is S*. This may be translated into

$$(x)(x \text{ is } S \supset (x)(x \text{ is } S))$$

In this sentence, the different occurrences of "x" are bound by different quantifiers of the same variable. When a variable occurs in the scope of two or more quantifiers of that same variable, it is bound by the nearest quantifier.

Once again, consider the statement $(x)(x$ is a dog $\supset x$ barks). The scope of the statement, "x is a dog $\supset x$ barks", will be satisfied by each object in the range of the variable, unless there be a case of a non-barking dog. However, that such a case exists is what our A statement denies. Compare this explanation with the Venn diagram which we used before to represent the meaning of an A statement. Notice that in a universe such as the one represented by Figure 11, the formula "x is a dog $\supset x$ barks"

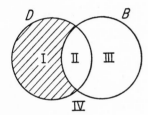

FIGURE 11

would be universally satisfied. The antecedent, "x is a dog", could not be satisfied in region I, for there would be no object in that region. Hence, the implication as a whole could not be falsified by anything in that region. It is easy to see that if there were objects in any other region depicted by the diagram, they would have to satisfy the scope of the statement, "$(x)(x$ is a dog $\supset x$ barks)". Consequently, one sees that that statement has the same meaning as the Venn diagram.

The E statement, "No dogs bark", may be expressed by "$(x)(x$ is a dog $\supset x$ does not bark)". We note in the case both of A and E statements that these statements do not imply that their subject classes have members. We describe this fact by saying that A and E statements lack existential import. Of course, when a person says that all dogs bark, he may be presumed to know that there are dogs, but what he states is that nothing is a dog unless it barks. And this statement may be interpreted as leaving open the question of the existence of dogs.

To represent the meanings of I and O statements, we utilize the particular quantifier "$(\exists x)$". *Some S is P* may be rendered by $(\exists x)\,(x$ is an S and x is $P)$ which may be read:

For some x, x is an S and x is a P.

or

For at least one choice of x, x is an S and x is a P.

The I statement is true if and only if the scope of the quantifier is satisfied by at least one thing in the range of the variable of quantification.

The O statement is similarly interpreted. *Some S is not P* may be rendered by

$(\exists x)\,(x$ is S and x is not $P)$

Whereas A and E statements lack existential import, the I and O forms of statement do have such existential import. These particular statements are true, we have said, just in case an object in the range of the variable of quantification satisfies the scope of the quantifier. But in the case of I and O statements the scopes are conjunctions. To satisfy a conjunction, an object must satisfy each factor of the conjunction. Hence, for "some dogs bark" to be true, there must be a dog. The reason for the difference between universal and particular subject-predicate statements in respect to existential import has to do, *not* with the difference between universal and particular quantifiers, but with the formal difference between the scopes of the quantifiers in the A, E, I, O schedule of statements. Thus, we should expect to find no difference in existential import between the statements

$(x)\,(x$ is S and x is $P)$

and

$(\exists x)\,(x$ is S and x is $P)$

In this case, their scopes have the same logical form. But whereas the second of these statements is an I statement, the first does not belong in the schedule of subject-predicate forms of statement. In fact, there is no difference in existential import between these statements. We must, therefore, make an effort to remember that the scopes of A and E statements are implication formulae, whereas the scopes of I and O statements are conjunctions.

One other terminological detail. Instead of saying that x has the property F we shall frequently find it convenient to write $F(x)$.

The following table summarizes the preceding discussion:

A	All S is P	$(x)(Sx \supset Px)$	Does not imply that the subject class has members.
E	No S is P	$(x)(Sx \supset \sim Px)$	As above.
I	Some S is P	$(\exists x)(Sx \cdot Px)$	Does imply that the subject class has members.
O	Some S is not P	$(\exists x)(Sx \cdot \sim Px)$	As above.

EXERCISES

Use Venn diagrams to explain why the following argument forms are non-validating forms:

1 ALL S IS P.
   NO Q IS P.
   ───────────────
   SOME S IS NOT Q.

2 THERE ARE P'S.
   ALL P IS S.
   ALL Q IS P.
   ───────────────
   SOME Q IS S.

3 THERE ARE P'S.
   NO S IS Q.
   ALL P IS Q.
   ───────────────
   SOME S IS NOT P.

4 SOME S IS NOT P.
   NO S IS Q.
   ───────────────
   SOME P IS NOT Q.

Instead of utilizing Venn diagrams, we shall formulate certain validating forms of argument which are more powerful than the

Venn method. We shall use the following rules:

1. The Adjunctive Principle.
2. The Implicative Principle.
3. The Applicative Principle.
4. The Diagonal Principle.
5. The Dequantification Principle.

After explaining the first four of these forms of argument, we shall apply them first to very simple sorts of arguments, such as syllogisms which can also be tested by the Venn method. Then in the following chapter we shall explain the Dequantification Principle and discuss the application of our principles to more complicated problems.

The Adjunctive Principle

Let us use the syntactical variables, "A", "B", "C", etc., to designate not only complete sentences, as we have done in the past, but also the incomplete sentences which contain variables and which may occur as the scopes of quantifiers. We assume that the following argument forms are validating forms:

I	II	III
$(x)(A)$	$(x)(A)$	$(x)(A)$
$(x)(B)$	$(x)(B)$	$(\exists x)(B)$
$(x)(A \cdot B)$	$(\exists x)(A \cdot B)$	$(\exists x)(A \cdot B)$

In other words, if we have two premisses, utilizing the same variable of quantification, and if at least one of the premisses is universal, then we may, in the conclusion, conjoin their scopes under a single quantifier. When we apply the Adjunctive Principle, the quantifier of the conclusion must be particular if one of the premisses is particular. Otherwise, the conclusion may be either universal or particular. That argument II is valid depends upon the circumstance that the premisses are uninterpreted unless a non-empty range of values is associated with the variables which occur therein. For example, the following argument is valid by adjunction.

$$(x)(Sx \supset Px)$$
$$(x)(Px \supset Qx)$$
$$\overline{(\exists x)((Sx \supset Px) \cdot (Px \supset Qx))}$$

The Implicative Principle

If $A \supset B$ is a tautology, then the following arguments are valid:

IV	V	VI
$(x)(A)$	$(x)(A)$	$(\exists x)(A)$
$(x)(B)$	$(\exists x)(B)$	$(\exists x)(B)$

We note that the reason for the validity of V is that interpreting the premiss involves associating a non-empty range of values to the variable "x". The following is an example of the use of the Implicative Principle:

$$(x)(Sx \supset \sim Px)$$
$$\overline{(x)(Px \supset \sim Sx)}$$

The argument is of pattern IV. The variable "A" corresponds to the formula $Sx \supset \sim Px$. The variable "B" corresponds to the formula $Px \supset \sim Sx$. We note that the implication sentence

$$(Sx \supset \sim Px) \supset (Px \supset \sim Sx)$$

is a tautology. Hence, the requirement that $A \supset B$ be tautological is satisfied in this case.

The Applicative Principle

That which holds in every case must hold in the case of an object designated by name. We may state the Applicative Principle more exactly as follows: let f_x be a formula containing occurrences of "x" which are not bound by quantifiers occurring in f_x. Let $f_x(a)$ be the result of applying this formula to the name, a, which designates an object in the range of "x". That is,

$f_x(a)$ is the result of substituting a for "x" in f_x. Then the following argument is valid:

$$\frac{(x)\,(f_x)}{f_x(a)}$$

For example,

$$\frac{(x)\,(x \text{ IS HUMAN} \supset x \text{ IS MORTAL})}{\text{JOHN IS HUMAN} \supset \text{JOHN IS MORTAL}}$$

The Diagonal Principle

Let us think of universal and particular quantifiers as opposite to one another. Then we may state the diagonal principle as follows: The denial of a general statement may be expressed by altering the quantifiers in the quantificational prefix to quantifiers of the opposite sort and then denying the scope. For example, the denial of

$$(\exists x)\,(y)\,(\exists z)\,(Sx\!:\!Qy \supset Sz)$$

may be written

$$(x)\,(\exists y)\,(z)\,(\sim (Sx\!:\!Qy \supset Sz))$$

The reason for the choice of the name "Diagonal Principle" for this rule will become apparent later when we discuss the square of opposition. It is possible to apply the principles which we have so far discussed to a wide range of cases before we consider the Dequantification Principle and its applications.

The Syllogism

The first application which we shall make of the Adjunctive Principle and the Implicative Principle is the theory of syllogism. Since we have gained some familiarity with this type of argument in connection with our discussion of Venn diagrams, the purpose of the present discussion is to throw light on the meaning and use of our principles rather than to extend our knowledge of our subject matter.

A syllogism is an argument having two premisses and a con-clusion. These premisses and the conclusion are of the subject-predicate form. Furthermore, a syllogism contains just three terms: the major term, which is the predicate of the conclusion, the minor term, which is the subject of the conclusion, and the middle term, which occurs in both premisses. For example,

ALL CHILDREN ARE NAIVE.

NO NAIVE PERSON IS PHILOSOPHICAL.

NO CHILDREN ARE PHILOSOPHICAL.

is a syllogism.

We note that the major term is "philosophical", that the minor term is "children", and that the middle term is "naive". The major premiss is the premiss which contains the major term. The minor premiss contains the minor term. The middle term serves as a link to connect the major and minor terms. The con-clusion of the syllogism eliminates the middle term and estab-lishes a direct relation between the minor and major terms. Syllogistic inference is essentially a process of eliminating the middle term. We proceed to study this process in detail.

If we translate the premisses into the idiom of quantification, we obtain as our premisses:

(1) $\qquad\qquad (x)(Cx \supset Nx)$

(2) $\qquad\qquad (x)(Nx \supset \sim Px)$

We then combine the above premisses in accordance with the Adjunctive Principle to obtain

(3) $\qquad\qquad (x)((Cx \supset Nx) \cdot (Nx \supset \sim Px))$

Now we can easily verify that the following formula is tautological.

$$((Cx \supset Nx) \cdot (Nx \supset \sim Px)) \supset (Cx \supset \sim Px)$$

It is, in fact, a special case of the principle of transitivity noticed earlier. Now, by virtue of the tautological character of this formula, the Implicative Principle authorizes us to infer from (3) the statement

(4) $\qquad\qquad (x)(Cx \supset \sim Px)$

which says that no child is philosophical. We have, then, by a series of arguments, each authorized by our rules, obtained the conclusion of the syllogism. Hence, we conclude that syllogism is valid.

Let us consider another example:

NO GOATS EAT TIN CANS.

SOME GOATS ARE PLAYFUL.

SOME PLAYFUL BEINGS DO NOT EAT TIN CANS.

The premisses of the argument may be paraphrased as

(1) $\qquad\qquad (x)(Gx \supset \sim Tx)$

(2) $\qquad\qquad (\exists x)(Gx \cdot Px)$

By the Adjunctive Principle we obtain

(3) $\qquad\qquad (\exists x)((Gx \supset \sim Tx) \cdot Gx \cdot Px)$

The reader may easily satisfy himself that the following formula is tautological:

$$[(Gx \supset \sim Tx) \cdot (Gx \cdot Px)] \supset (Px \cdot \sim Tx)$$

Therefore, using the Implicative Principle, we obtain from (3) the conclusion $(\exists x)(Px \cdot \sim Tx)$, which says that some playful beings do not eat tin cans.

SUMMARY

If an argument is valid by virtue of its syllogistic form, then it has one of the following forms:

$(x)(A)$	$(x)(A)$
$(x)(B)$	$(\exists x)(B)$
$(x)(C)$	$(\exists x)(C)$

and the following additional conditions are satisfied:

1. $A \cdot B$ tautologically implies C.
2. The premisses of the syllogism are subject-predicate in form.

3. Three and only three terms occur in the argument. These terms are the major, minor, and middle terms.

4. The conclusion eliminates the middle term.

The reader will note that an argument of the form

$(x)(A)$
$(x)(B)$
$\overline{(\exists x)(C)}$

may be valid, but it can be shown to be asyllogistic.

Enthymemes

An enthymeme is an argument not all of whose premisses are expressly stated. For example, if one were to argue that since all men are mortal, John is mortal, one would, no doubt, be taking it for granted that John is a man. It would, therefore, be pointless pedantry to say what is in fact the case, that the argument as stated is invalid. The argument as stated is not the argument intended. It would, in practice, be understood that only a fragment of the argument intended had been presented.

In criticizing arguments which occur in life, one must be guided not only by a sense of logical form but also by sensitivity to language. It rarely happens that we state all of the premisses of our arguments. In order to criticize an argument, one must very often construe it as an enthymeme and restore to it those tacit premisses which are essential to its validity. There is no simple rule by which to decide whether an argument should be interpreted as an enthymeme, with tacit premisses, and valid, or whether it should be interpreted as a completely formulated argument and invalid. One must be guided by tact and by one's knowledge of the context of the discussion. Consider the example:

ALL TRADITIONAL LOGIC BOOKS EMPHASIZE THE IMPORTANCE OF SYLLOGISM.

NO MODERN TEXT EMPHASIZES THE IMPORTANCE OF SYLLOGISM.

SOME MODERN TEXTS ARE NOT TRADITIONAL LOGIC BOOKS.

It is easy to verify that from the premisses we can validly

obtain the conclusion, "No modern text is a traditional logic book". But we cannot properly advance from this E statement to the O statement, "Some modern texts are not traditional logic books". The reason is that E statements have been interpreted as lacking existential import, whereas O statements have been interpreted as possessing existential import. Should we then say that the argument is invalid? It appears more credible to interpret the argument as an enthymeme containing the tacit premiss, "There are modern texts". So supplemented, the argument is valid, though it is no longer a syllogism, since it possesses three premisses.

Traditional logic and modern logic differ systematically in respect to the question of existential import. The reason for this may be that traditional logic does not possess the concept of an empty class. The practical importance of this distinction between traditional and modern logic is somewhat mitigated by the consideration that arguments which are pronounced valid by traditional logic and invalid by the modern school are arguments which we may often classify as enthymematic, valid in the context of extraneous assumption.

EXERCISES

State additional premisses needed for the following arguments to be valid.

1. All of the testimony presented in court is correct. Therefore, some of Jones's statements must have been correct.

2. All of my cousins are your cousins. All of your cousins are talented. Therefore, some of my cousins are talented.

3. All poets are hypersensitive. No one is a poet unless he has the capacity to form vivid images. Therefore, some who have this capacity are hypersensitive.

4. None of the guilty will go unpunished. Either the witness lied or all of the defendants will go unpunished. Therefore, none of the defendants are guilty.

5. If the witness told the truth, all members of the Martin family are guilty. But since no members of the Martin family are guilty, the witness lied.

Syllogisms with One Premiss Singular

Take an argument such as:

ALL MEN ARE MORTAL.

SOCRATES IS A MAN.

SOCRATES IS MORTAL.

The premisses may be represented thus:

(x) (Man $x \supset$ Mortal x)
Man Socrates

By the Applicative Principle we obtain from the major premiss

Man (Socrates) $\supset$ Mortal (Socrates)

This statement, together with the minor premiss of the argument, gives the desired conclusion.

Sorites

An argument, having more than two premisses and such that the derivation of the conclusion from the premisses consists of a sequence of syllogistic arguments, is called a sorites.

EXERCISES

Discuss the validity of the following arguments, which are derived from Lewis Carroll's *Symbolic Logic.**

1 SHOWY TALKERS THINK TOO MUCH OF THEMSELVES.

NO REALLY WELL-INFORMED PEOPLE ARE BAD COMPANY.

PEOPLE WHO THINK TOO MUCH OF THEMSELVES ARE NOT GOOD COMPANY.

SHOWY TALKERS ARE NOT REALLY WELL-INFORMED.
(*Let the Universe of Discourse consist of persons.*)

2 NO EXPERIENCED PERSON IS INCOMPETENT.

JENKINS IS ALWAYS BLUNDERING.

NO COMPETENT PERSON IS ALWAYS BLUNDERING.

JENKINS IS INEXPERIENCED.

* From *The Complete Works of Lewis Carroll*, Random House, Inc.

3   NO SHARK EVER DOUBTS THAT IT IS WELL FITTED OUT.

A FISH THAT CANNOT DANCE A MINUET IS CONTEMPTIBLE.

NO FISH IS QUITE CERTAIN THAT IT IS WELL FITTED OUT, UNLESS IT HAS THREE ROWS OF TEETH.

ALL FISHES, EXCEPT SHARKS, ARE KIND TO CHILDREN.

NO HEAVY FISH CAN DANCE A MINUET.

A FISH WITH THREE ROWS OF TEETH IS NOT TO BE DESPISED.

NO HEAVY FISH IS UNKIND TO CHILDREN.

(Let the Universe of Discourse consist of fishes.)

4   WHEN I WORK A LOGIC EXAMPLE WITHOUT GRUMBLING, YOU MAY BE SURE IT IS ONE THAT I CAN UNDERSTAND.

THESE SORITES ARE NOT ARRANGED IN REGULAR ORDER, AS THE EXAMPLES I AM USED TO ARE.

NO EASY EXAMPLE EVER MAKES MY HEAD ACHE.

I CAN'T UNDERSTAND EXAMPLES THAT ARE NOT ARRANGED IN REGULAR ORDER, AS THOSE I AM USED TO ARE.

I NEVER GRUMBLE AT AN EXAMPLE, UNLESS IT GIVES ME A HEADACHE.

THESE SORITES EXAMPLES ARE DIFFICULT.

(Let the Universe of Discourse consist of logic examples worked by me.)

5   NO ONE WHO IS GOING TO A PARTY EVER FAILS TO BRUSH HIS HAIR.

NO ONE LOOKS FASCINATING IF HE IS UNTIDY.

OPIUM-EATERS HAVE NO SELF-COMMAND.

EVERYONE WHO HAS BRUSHED HIS HAIR LOOKS FASCINATING.

NO ONE WEARS WHITE KID GLOVES, UNLESS HE IS GOING TO A PARTY.

A MAN IS ALWAYS UNTIDY IF HE HAS NO SELF-COMMAND.

OPIUM-EATERS NEVER WEAR WHITE KID GLOVES.

(Let the Universe of Discourse consist of persons.)

6   NO KITTEN THAT LOVES FISH IS UNTEACHABLE.

NO KITTEN WITHOUT A TAIL WILL PLAY WITH A GORILLA.

KITTENS WITH WHISKERS ALWAYS LOVE FISH.

NO TEACHABLE KITTEN HAS GREEN EYES.

NO KITTENS HAVE TAILS UNLESS THEY HAVE WHISKERS.

NO KITTEN WITH GREEN EYES WILL PLAY WITH A GORILLA.

(Let the Universe of Discourse consist of kittens.)

Immediate Inference

The name "immediate inference" is used to denote certain arguments which have a single subject-predicate premiss and a subject-predicate conclusion. The more important of these we shall now study. These arguments involve the use of no new principle; they merely illustrate the rules of inference which have been already laid down.

CONVERSION

Conversion consists of the simple interchange of subject and predicate. The statement on which this operation is performed is called the verse. The result of the operation is called the converse. The converse of *No S is P* is *No P is S*. Conversion is not always a valid mode of inference. For example, from the statement, "Some humans are not geniuses", it cannot validly be deduced that some geniuses are not human. But it is easy to verify that conversion can validly be applied to E and I statements.

The statement *No S is P* can be translated into $(x)(Sx \supset \sim Px)$. By the use of the Principle of Transposition and the Implicative Principle, we may infer $(x)(Px \supset \sim Sx)$, which is the same as *No P is S*. Hence, an E statement may be converted.

By a similar use of the Implicative Principle, one can justify application of conversion upon I statements. That A and O statements cannot in general be converted is shown by counter examples. Such a counter example has already been indicated for the case of O statements. The reader should construct an example to show that conversion of A statements is not a validating form of argument.

CONVERSION BY LIMITATION

There is a type of argument which goes by the name of "conversion by limitation" which we shall now describe. If our premisses are *All S is P* and *There are S's*, we may then infer *Some P is S*. The operation consists of converting the A premiss and altering its quantity. The reader should verify that the conclusion follows from the premisses by the use of the Adjunctive and Implicative Principles. Such inference is not, however, immediate inference in the strict sense, since the argument has two premisses. But in traditional logic it was thought to be a form of immediate inference, since it was supposed that A statements have existential import. It is true that in everyday discourse A statements are converted by limitation without explicit expression of any existence assumption. Such an argument may be construed as an enthymeme.

QUALITY AND QUANTITY

On page 38 of this chapter, it was pointed out that the quality of a statement refers to whether that statement is affirmative or negative. Thus A and I statements are positive or affirmative in quality, whereas E and O statements are of negative quality.

NEGATIVE TERMS

In logic, as in ordinary language, it is customary to employ negative terms. Thus, instead of saying that Quasimodo was not beautiful, we could as well say that he was non-beautiful, the hyphenated term being a negative predicate. It is usual in logic to write, instead of "non-F", "$-F$". It is important to note the contrast between the opposite of a given term and its negative. Thus, "ugly" is the opposite of "beautiful", not its negative. A pebble may be neither beautiful nor ugly. In that case, it will be non-beautiful. We stipulate that

$$-F(x) \text{ is definitionally equivalent to } \sim F(x)$$

Now we may explain that to alter the sign of a predicate is to place a negative sign before it or to erase one if there be one already there.

OBVERSION

To obvert a statement we alter both its quality and the sign of its predicate. Obversion may be validly performed upon A, E, I, and O statements. The following table indicates the result of obverting these four kinds of statements. It is left as an exercise for the reader to verify that obversion is a valid operation.

Verse	*Obverse*
All S is P	No S is − P
No S is P	All S is − P
Some S is P	Some S is not − P
Some S is not P	Some S is − P

CONTRAPOSITION

This operation consists of interchanging subject and predicate and altering the sign of each. Thus, the contrapositive of *All S is P* is *All − P is − S*. The contrapositive of *Some S is not P* is *Some − P is not − S*. Contraposition may validly be performed only in the case of A and O statements. To verify this fact is left as an exercise for the reader.

CONTRAPOSITION BY LIMITATION

Contraposition may not validly be applied to an E statement, but the following inference is valid.

NO S IS P.

THERE ARE S'S.

SOME − P IS NOT − S.

The inference is strictly not immediate, since the argument has two premisses. But sometimes it is encountered in enthymematic form with the existence assumption tacit.

The Square of Opposition

The statement, *A logically implies B*, signifies that the statement

if *A* then necessarily *B*

is true.

The statement, *A logically precludes B*, signifies that the statement

if *A* then necessarily ∼ *B*

is true.

To say that *A* is logically equivalent to *B* means the same as to say that *A* logically implies and is logically implied by *B*.

Two statements are logically independent of one another just in case the affirmation or denial of the one is not derivable from the affirmation or denial of the other.

We say that two statements, *A* and *B*, are logically opposed or logically contrary to one another just in case *A* logically precludes *B*, but the denial of *A* does not logically preclude the denial of *B*. In other words, *A* and *B* are logically opposed just in case *A* and *B* form an inconsistent set while their denials form a consistent set. Thus, "Smith is moral" is contrary to

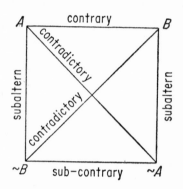

FIGURE 12

"Smith is immoral". These statements cannot both be true. But their denials can both be true.

Two statements are said to be contradictory to one another if and only if one of them is logically equivalent to the denial of the other. A frequently committed fallacy consists in confusing contradictory statements with contrary statements. It is not necessary that one of a pair of contraries be true. But in the case of contradictories, one must be true and one false.

Statements are said to be subcontrary to one another if and only if their denials are contraries of one another. In other words, subcontrary statements can both be true, but they cannot both be false.

If the statement *A* logically implies *B* but is not in turn logically implied by *B*, then *B* is called subaltern to *A*.

Let *A* and *B* be two statements which are contraries; then the square of opposition shown in Figure 12 expresses relations holding between *A* and *B*.

The vertices of the square represent the statements A, B, $\sim A$, and $\sim B$. By hypothesis, A and B are contrary. By the definition of subcontrariety, $\sim A$ and $\sim B$ are subcontraries. By construction, the diagonal lines connect contradictories. That $\sim B$ is subaltern to A follows from the fact that A and B are contrary, for the contrariety of A and B implies that A logically precludes B, which means that A logically implies $\sim B$. Furthermore, $\sim B$ cannot in the present case logically imply A; the meaning of logical implication is such that it would then be impossible for $\sim B$ to be true and A to be false. This is to say it would be impossible to have A and B each false. But it must

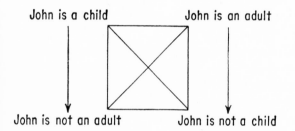

John is a child   John is an adult

John is not an adult   John is not a child   FIGURE 13

be possible for A and B each to be false, or A and B would not be contrary. By the same token, that $\sim A$ is subaltern to B follows from the contrariety between A and B.

For example, the statements A and B might be "John is a child" and "John is an adult". These are contrary statements, since it would be inconsistent for both statements to be true but consistent for both to be false. Then the statements "John is not a child" and "John is not an adult" are subcontrary. These can both be true but they cannot both be false. The statements can be arranged to form a square of opposition, as shown in Figure 13.

The diagonal lines connect contradictories. The horizontal lines connect contraries or subcontraries. The vertical arrows connect the original statements with statements which are subaltern to them. If John is a child, then necessarily John is not an adult. But if John is not an adult, it does not follow that John is a child. Hence, "John is not an adult" is subaltern to "John is a child". And, similarly, "John is not a child" is subaltern to "John is an adult".

We turn next to the question whatever we can arrange A, E, I, and O statements so as to form a square of opposition. It is easy to verify by the diagonal principle that A and O are contradic-

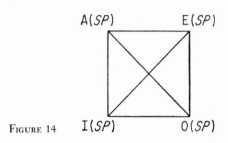

FIGURE 14

tory and that E and I are contradictory. This fact suggests the arrangement illustrated in Figure 14.

However, since A(*SP*) lacks existential import, I(*SP*) is not derivable from A(*SP*), so the relations of subalternation and contrariety and subcontrariety do not hold. Hence, we do not have here a true square of opposition.

We may, however, construct a quasi-square of opposition. This is to say that, in an argument in which we have the premiss ∃(*x*)(*Sx*), I(*SP*) is *as if* it were subaltern to A(*SP*), E(*SP*) is as if it were contrary to A(*SP*), O(*SP*) is as if it were subcontrary to I(*SP*), and O(*SP*) is as if it were subaltern to E(*SP*). Hence, we speak, in such cases, of quasi-subalternation, quasi-contrariety and quasi-subcontrariety.

EXERCISE

Discuss the validity of

A ⊃ ALL *S* IS *P*.
NO *S* IS *P*.
_____
∼ A

If we construe the preceding argument as an enthymeme so that the assumption (∃*x*)(*Sx*) is tacit, the argument is valid. For by the relation of quasi-contrariety, the second premiss permits us to deny the consequent of the first premiss.

The student should note that Figure 15 is a genuine square of opposition, provided that neither $(x)(A)$ nor $(x)(\sim A)$ is a logically necessary statement.

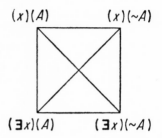

FIGURE 15

That the relations of subalternation hold is due to the circumstance that the range of the variable "x" is non-empty. We must note, however, that the statements

$$(x)(A)$$
$$(x)(\sim A)$$
$$(\exists x)(A)$$
$$(\exists x)(\sim A)$$

do not correspond to the forms A, E, I, and O. For example, if A is the formula $Sx \supset Px$, then $(x)(A)$ is an A statement. But $(x)(\sim A)$ is $(x)(Sx \cdot \sim Px)$, which is not an E statement. Also, $(\exists x)(A)$ is, by the Diagonal Principle, $(\exists x)(Sx \supset Px)$, which is not an I statement. However, $(\exists x)(\sim A)$ is the O statement, $(\exists x)(Sx \cdot \sim Px)$.

EXERCISES

1   Classify the logical relationships obtaining in the following pairs of statements, utilizing the concepts of subalternation, contrariety, contradiction, subcontrariety, equivalence, implication, and independence.

   a.   Tom is blue-eyed; Tom is brown-eyed.

    b. This substance is non-metallic; this substance is non-wooden.

    c. John is clever; if John did it, he is clever.

    d. All chimps are furry; no chimps are furry.

    e. John is clever; Tom isn't.

    f. All men know fear; those who know not fear are not men.

2 Discuss the validity of the following arguments:

    a. If some witnesses lie, then no politician is safe. All politicians lie. Some politicians are witnesses. Therefore, some liars are not safe.

    b. If some witnesses did not lie, then all of the witnesses were confused. No witness was confused. Some of the witnesses were illiterate. Hence, some illiterate people were liars.

3 Simplify the following sentences:

    a. No non-barker is a dog.

    b. All non-barkers are non-dogs.

    c. Some who don't bark are not in the class of non-dogs.

4 The international bottle club is so selective that its members satisfy the following rules:

    a. A member when drunk cannot tell the difference beween left and right.

    b. A member who cannot tell the difference between night and day is drunk.

    c. Each member must be either unable to tell the difference between left and right or unable to tell the difference between day and night.

    Show that no member of the club can tell the difference between left and right.

3

Dequantification

In the preceding chapter, we have discussed syllogistic argument. But, as we know, we might have validated syllogistic arguments by the method of countersets. Let us do so now as a preliminary to explaining the method of dequantification. Consider the argument

$(x)(Sx \supset Px)$
$(x)(Qx \supset \sim Px)$
$\overline{(x)(Qx \supset \sim Sx)}$

We consider the counterset of this argument.

(1) $(x)(Sx \supset Px)$ (All S is P.)

(2) $(x)(Qx \supset \sim Px)$ (No Q is P.)

(3) $(\exists x)(Qx \cdot Sx)$

Combining (2) and (3) by the Adjunctive Principle, we obtain

(4) $(\exists x)((Qx \cdot Sx \cdot (Qx \supset \sim Px))$

which by the Implicative Rule yields

(5) $(\exists x)(Sx \cdot \sim Px)$ (Some S is not P.)

Since (5) is the contradictory of (1), by the Diagonal Principle, we have shown the counterset to be inconsistent, and, therefore, the original argument must have been valid.

The method of dequantification is not very different from the procedure just discussed. Instead, however, of steps (4) and (5) we can proceed in this manner. Sentence (3) of the counterset says that there exists an object, x, satisfying the condition, $Qx \cdot Sx$. Let x_0 be such an object satisfying this condition. The symbol "x_0" is called an *arbitrary constant*. It is to be treated in our calculations *as if* it were a proper name, although, in fact, it is a variable.

We have, then,

(4') $Qx_0 \cdot Sx_0$

We may then use sentence (1) to infer, by the Applicative Principle,

(5') $Sx_0 \supset Px_0$

The reasoning is that (1) says that everything satisfies the condition $Sx \supset Px$. The Applicative Principle enables us to infer that in particular x_0 must satisfy this condition. By a similar argument, we derive from (2) the sentence

(6') $Qx_0 \supset \sim Px_0$

But now the reader can easily verify by a truth-table calculation that sentences (4'), (5'), and (6') are inconsistent. The counterset is in this way shown to be inconsistent and the original argument valid. The method of dequantification is, therefore, a method of validating an argument. The method consists in carrying out a sequence of steps or operations.

Step 1. Form the counterset of the argument. If any sentence in this counterset is of the form $\sim (x)A$, use the Diagonal Principle and rewrite it in the form $(\exists x)(\sim A)$. If any sentence in the counterset is of the form $\sim (\exists x)A$, rewrite it as $(x)(\sim A)$.

Step 2. If any sentence of the form $(\exists x)(A)$ occurs as a member of the counterset, or as a factor of a conjunction which, in turn, is a member of the counterset, delete the quantifier and substitute an arbitrary constant for the variable of quantification. However, if more than one existential quantifier is deleted, care must be taken to substitute *distinct* arbitrary constants.

Step 3. Attempt now to apply the universal quantifiers which occur in the counterset to the arbitrary constants which have been introduced. This may be done by taking those sentences of the form $(x)B$ which are members of the counterset (or which are factors of conjunctions which are members of the counterset) and eliminating their quantifiers by the Applicative Principle, substituting for the variables of quantification the arbitrary constants.

Step 4. The result of eliminating quantifiers is a set of formulae whose inconsistency one may now seek to determine by the use of truth tables.

EXAMPLE:

(x) (SOCRATES WAS HUMAN $\supset$ (x IS A PHILOSOPHER $\supset$ x IS HUMAN)).

SOCRATES WAS HUMAN.

THEREFORE, (x) (x IS A PHILOSOPHER $\supset$ x IS HUMAN).

The counterset is

(1) $\qquad\qquad (x)(s \supset (Px \supset Hx))$

(2) $\qquad\qquad\qquad s$

(3) $\qquad\qquad (\exists x)(Px \cdot \sim Hx)$

The first step is to delete "$(\exists x)$" from (3) and substitute "x_0" for "x" in the scope of the quantifier. We then apply the universal quantifier in sentence (1) to the arbitrary constant, by virtue of the Applicative Principle. We then obtain

(4) $\qquad\qquad Px_0 \cdot \sim Hx_0$

(5) $\qquad\qquad s \supset (Px_0 \supset Hx_0)$

By the method of asserting the antecedent and by using (2) and (5), we obtain $Px_0 \supset Hx_0$, which contradicts (4). The demonstrated inconsistency of the counterset proves the validity of the argument.

EXAMPLE:

$\qquad\qquad (\exists x)(Fx) \vee (\exists x)(Gx)$

Therefore,

$\qquad\qquad (\exists x)(Fx \vee Gx)$

The counterset is (if we use the Diagonal and Implicative Principles) expressible in the form:

(1) $(\exists x)(Fx) \vee (\exists x)(Gx)$

(2) $(x)(\sim Fx \cdot \sim Gx)$

We cannot proceed by the elimination of the particular quantifiers in (1). For (1) does not say that there exists an object satisfying a condition. It says that *either* there exists such an object having the property F, *or* $(\exists x)(Gx)$. For a particular quantifier to be eliminable, it must be in the initial position of an asserted context. That is, it must occur in initial position in a formula which is either a member of a counterset or a factor in a conjunction which is a member of the counterset. If the existential quantifier occurs in an alternative of an alternation, it does not occur in eliminable position.

However, the counterset is, in fact, inconsistent. For, as we shall demonstrate in the following two examples, (2) is logically equivalent to

$$(x)(\sim Fx) \cdot (x)(\sim Gx)$$

which is the contradictory of (1).

EXAMPLE:

$$(x)(Fx \cdot Gx)$$

Therefore,

$$(x)(Fx) \cdot (x)(Gx)$$

From the premiss of this argument, we can obtain by means of the Implicative Principle the conclusion $(x)(Fx)$. In precisely the same way we may obtain $(x)(Gx)$. From the conclusions we obtain $(x)(Fx) \cdot (x)(Gx)$, by use of the Fundamental Principle.

EXAMPLE:

$$(x)Fx \cdot (x)Gx$$

Therefore,

$$(x)(Fx \cdot Gx)$$

The counterset of this argument is

(1) $(x)Fx \cdot (x)Gx$

(2) $(\exists x)(Fx \supset \sim Gx)$

From (1) we obtain by the Fundamental Principle

(3) $(x)Fx$

(4) $(x)Gx$

We now eliminate the particular quantifier in (2) by the method of dequantification and obtain

(5) $Fx_0 \supset \sim Gx_0$

Using the Applicative Principle, we apply the universal quantifiers of (3) and (4) to x_0. We derive

(6) Fx_0

(7) Gx_0

A truth-table analysis suffices to show the inconsistency of (5), (6), and (7). The counterset is inconsistent, therefore, and the argument is valid. The result of this and the preceding example is that the proposition $(x)Fx \cdot (x)Gx$ is logically equivalent to the proposition $(x)(Fx \cdot Gx)$.

In a more rigorous treatment of logic, this method of dequantification can be developed without employing the idea of an "arbitrary constant". But the device of arbitrary constants is useful for evoking an intuitive grasp of a most important type of argument. Once in possession of the "hang of the subject", the student should then reach for a more precise formulation of the methods discussed in this book.

Relations

Relational predicates may be of degree higher than 2, but in this book we shall consider only binary relations, that is, relations having only two subjects. Relational statements may be totally general, partially general, or totally singular. For example, a totally singular relational statement is "Smith killed Jones", where "Smith" and "Jones" are proper names. Examples of partially general relational statements are "Smith killed a man" and "Everybody likes Mary". On the other hand, "Some people like all children" or "Nobody is admired by everybody" are totally general relational statements. Let us consider how

such relational statements may be represented in terms of our
logical notation.

If R is a relation and "a" and "b" are proper names designating individuals, then "aRb" is the statement that a is R to b.

"Some S is R to a" asserts, evidently, that some S has a relational property. The statement, when it is so considered, is an
I statement. It says that there is some object which is S and
also is R to a. The statement may, therefore, be written
"$(\exists x)(Sx \cdot xRa)$". "Some S is not R to a" may be similarly
interpreted.

"Every S is R to a" asserts that every S has a certain relational property. When so considered, it is an A statement and
does not assert the existence of S's. The statement means that
if there are any S's, they are in the relation R to a. Therefore,
we may write it as "$(x)(Sx \supset xRa)$".

Similarly, "No S is R to a" may be expressed as "$(x)(Sx \supset$
$\sim xRa)$".

In just the same way, we may interpret the statements "a is R
to every S", "a is R to no S", and "a is R to some S" by the
formulae

$$(x)(Sx \supset aRx)$$
$$(x)(Sx \supset \sim aRx)$$
$$(\exists x)(Sx \cdot aRx)$$

Totally general relational propositions may be classified into
eight exclusive classes.

RAA   RAI
Every F is R to some G.   Every F is R to some G.
RIA   RII
Some F is R to every G.   Some F is R to some G.
$\bar{R}$AA $\bar{R}$AI
No F is R to any G.   No F is R to all the G's.

or   or
   Every F is $\bar{R}$ to every G.   Every F is $\bar{R}$ to some G.
$\bar{R}$IA $\bar{R}$II
   Some F is $\bar{R}$ to all G's.   Some F is $\bar{R}$ to some G.
or
   Some F is R to no G.

In the above cases, we call F the referent class and G the relatum class of the relation. Also, we employ the letters, A, E, I, and O to indicate that a term is universal positive, universal negative, particular positive, and particular negative. "$\bar{R}$" is used to designate negative relations.

The statement "no person likes all animals" is of the REA form. But since this statement says the same as "every person doesn't like some animal or other", we group it together with $\bar{R}$AI.*

The interpretation of the meaning of these statements is analogous to the interpretation placed upon the A, E, I, and O forms in the preceding chapter. Take the RAA form for an example. This statement does not assert either that there are F's or that there are G's. It asserts only that, whatever x and y may be, if x is an F and y is a G, then x is in the relation R to y. The RAA statement is hypothetical in import. Therefore, in continuation of our policy, we shall construe it as a generalized statement of material implication. In other words, we shall symbolize the RAA proposition by a statement of the form

(i) $(x)(y)(Fx \cdot Gy \supset xRy)$

We can see that this interpretation is sound if we interpret RAA as saying that every F satisfies the condition of being R to every G. We can then construe the statement as being of the subject-predicate form, F being the subject and the predicate being the expression "the property of being R to every G".

---

* Note the difference between "no person likes all animals" and "no person likes any animal". The first of these is $\bar{R}$AI. The second is $\bar{R}$AA. In the text we used REA as synonymous with $\bar{R}$AI. But the use of the expression REA should hereafter be avoided because of its inherent tendency to become ambiguous.

The statement may then be represented thus:

(ii) $(x)(Fx \supset x$ has the property of being R to every $G)$

But to say "x has the property of being R to every G" means the same as "x is R to every G", which, as we know, means the same as $(y)(Gy \supset xRy)$. Substituting this last in (ii), we obtain:

(iii) $(x)(Fx \supset (y)(Gy \supset xRy))$

Now (i) and (iii) are interderivable, as we shall proceed to show.

To show the validity of the argument

$(x)(y)((Fx \cdot Gy) \supset xRy)$ therefore, $(x)(Fx \supset (y)(Gy \supset xRy))$

we construct the counterset of the argument, viz.,

(1) $(x)(y)((Fx \cdot Gy) \supset xRy)$

(2) $(\exists x)(Fx \cdot \sim (y)(Gy \supset xRy))$

Next, we eliminate the particular quantifier in (2), obtaining

(3) $Fx_0 \cdot \sim (y)(Gy \supset x_0Ry)$

The second factor of (3), by the Diagonal Principle, may be written

(4) $(\exists y)(Gy \cdot \sim x_0Ry)$

Eliminating the particular quantifier in (4), we have

(5) $Gy_0 \cdot \sim x_0Ry_0$

(Notice that the arbitrary constant substituted for "y" must be distinct from "x_0". We cannot assume that $x_0 = y_0$.)

We must now apply the universal quantifiers of (1) to x_0 and y_0 by the Applicative Principle. Whether the variable "x" in (1) is best applied to x_0 or to y_0 cannot be determined except by trial. We apply, first, "(x)" to x_0, obtaining, by the Applicative Principle,

(6) $(y)((Fx_0 \cdot Gy) \supset x_0Ry)$

Now, we use (6), applying "(y)" to y_0 by the Applicative

Principle, obtaining

(7) $\qquad (Fx_0 \cdot Gy_0) \supset x_0Ry_0$

In (3), Fx_0 is asserted. In (5), Gy_0 is asserted. The antecedent of (7) is, therefore, assertible, and we may infer

(8) $\qquad x_0Ry_0$

which is inconsistent with (5). The counterset's inconsistency exhibits the validity of the original argument.

In like manner, the converse of the above argument can be shown to be valid. That is, we may show that

$(x)(Fx \supset (y)(Gy \supset xRy))$ therefore, $(x)(y)((Fx \cdot Gy) \supset xRy)$

is a valid argument. The counterset of the argument is

(1) $\qquad (x)(Fx \supset (y)(Gy \supset xRy))$

(2) $\qquad \exists(x) \sim (y)(Fx \cdot Gy \supset xRy)$

By the method of dequantification, we obtain from (2)

(3) $\qquad \sim (y)(Fx_0 \cdot Gy \supset x_0Ry)$

which is equivalent to

(4) $\qquad (\exists y)(Fx_0 \cdot Gy \cdot \sim x_0Ry)$

Dequantifying (4), we have

(5) $\qquad Fx_0 \cdot Gy_0 \cdot \sim x_0Ry_0$

Now, we apply the universal quantifier in (1) to x_0. We have

(6) $\qquad Fx_0 \supset (y)(Gy \supset x_0Ry)$

From (5) and (6) we have

(7) $\qquad (y)(Gy \supset x_0Ry)$

By the Applicative Principle, we obtain from (7)

(8) $\qquad Gy_0 \supset x_0Ry_0$

Using (5) and (8), and the method of asserting the antecedent, we obtain x_0Ry_0, which is inconsistent with (5).

We have just shown that

$(x)(y)(Fx \cdot Gy \supset xRy)$ and $(x)(Fx \supset (y)(Gy \supset xRy))$

are logically equivalent propositions.

In like manner, we can interpret RAI either as

$$(x)(\exists y)(Fx \supset (Gy \cdot xRy)) \quad \text{or as} \quad (x)(Fx \supset (\exists y)(Gy \cdot xRy))$$

For these statements may be shown to be equivalent in the manner of the preceding discussion. RIA may similarly be expressed as

$$(\exists x)(y)(Fx \cdot (Gy \supset xRy)) \quad \text{or as} \quad (\exists x)(Fx \cdot (y)(Gy \supset xRy))$$

The equivalence of these statements may easily be demonstrated by the method of dequantification. The reader should satisfy himself on this point.

Similarly, RII may be written either as

$$(\exists x)(\exists y)(Fx \cdot Gy \cdot xRy) \quad \text{or as} \quad (\exists x)(Fx \cdot (\exists y)(Gy \cdot xRy))$$

The forms $\bar{R}AA$, $\bar{R}AI$, etc., are the same as the four preceding except that in the place of xRy we have $\sim xRy$. We may, therefore, construct the following table:

Form	English idiom	Logistic representation
RAA	Every F is R to every G.	$(x)(y)(Fx \cdot Gy \supset xRy)$
RAI	Every F is R to some G.	$(x)(\exists y)(Fx \supset (Gy \cdot xRy))$
RIA	Some F is R to every G.	$(\exists x)(y)(Fx \cdot (Gy \supset xRy))$
RII	Some F is R to some G.	$(\exists x)(\exists y)(Fx \cdot Gy \cdot xRy)$
$\bar{R}AA$	No F is R to a G. Each F is non-R to all G's.	$(x)(y)(Fx \cdot Gy \supset \sim xRy)$
$\bar{R}AI$	No F is R to every G. Every F is non-R to some G.	$(x)(\exists y)(Fx \supset (Gy \cdot \sim xRy))$
$\bar{R}IA$	Some F is R to no G. Some F is non-R to all G's.	$(\exists x)(y)(Fx \cdot (Gy \supset \sim xRy))$
$\bar{R}II$	Some F is non-R to some G.	$(\exists x)(\exists y)(Fx \cdot Gy \cdot \sim xRy)$

It is possible to represent the relations of these eight forms by means of an octagon of opposition, (Figure 16) which is a generalization of the square of opposition studied in the preceding chapter.

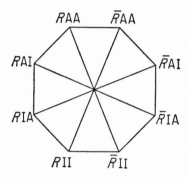

FIGURE 16

The reader will notice that the vertices of the octagon which are connected by diagonal lines represent contradictories. Thus the propositions

RIA: Some musicians hate all saxophonists.

and

$\bar{R}$AI: No musician hates all saxophonists.
(All musicians are non-haters of some saxophonists.)

are contradictories. The reader should verify that, in general, the diagonals of the octagon of opposition connect contradictory propositions.

The following exercises are intended to give the reader practice in applying the process of dequantification to relational arguments.

EXAMPLE:

Every horse is an animal. Therefore, all heads of horses are heads of animals.

The argument may be represented as follows:

$$(x)(Hx \supset Ax)$$

therefore,

$$(x)[(\exists z)(Hz \cdot xTz) \supset (\exists y)(Ay \cdot xTy)]$$

where H and A mean *horse* and *animal*, respectively, and T signifies the relation, *being the head of*.

The counterset of the argument is

(1) $$(x)\,(Hx \supset Ax)$$

(2) $$(\exists x)\,[(\exists z)\,(Hz \cdot xTz) \cdot (y)\,(Ay \supset x \sim Ty)]$$

By dequantification we obtain from (2)

(3) $$Hz_0 \cdot x_0 Tz_0 \cdot (y)\,(Ay \supset \sim x_0 Ty)$$

We apply the Applicative Principle, using (1) to obtain

(4) $$Hz_0 \supset Az_0$$

We apply the Applicative Principle, using the third factor of (3) to obtain

(5) $$Az_0 \supset \sim x_0 Tz_0$$

which, in conjunction with (4), gives

(6) $$Hz_0 \supset \sim x_0 Tz_0$$

But (3) and (6) are evidently contradictory. Hence, the counterset of the argument is inconsistent and the argument is valid.

EXERCISES

1   In my neighborhood, there are two groups, the Outs and the Ins. Everybody in the neighborhood is in one of these two groups, but nobody is in both. Furthermore, if anybody in the neighborhood orders an In to do anything, we know immediately that he himself is an In. One of my neighbors, Mr. X, obeyed an Out. What can the reader conclude about Mr. X? Is he an In or an Out? The reader must assume, of course, that if a person obeys another, he is ordered by that other.

2   In a town called Boston (not, of course, *the* Boston) there once dwelt five characters called Brown, Smith, Jones, Kelly, and Stephens, who were well known for their extraordinary solemnity. As a matter of fact, Brown was a charter member and president of the Bilious Club. To indicate the peculiarity of this club (and also of Boston) I may simply call attention to the fact that if any Bos-

tonian hated any member of the Bilious Club he promptly joined the club. But Smith, strange to tell, never joined the club, although he did hate Jones, who, in turn, hated Kelly, who, in turn, hated Stephens. In view of these facts, can the reader say whether Stephens hated Brown?

3 What existence assumption must be added to the premisses to convert the following argument into a valid one?

All S is R to all P. All P's are Q's. Therefore, every S is R to some Q.

4 Test the validity of the following argument.

$(x)[Fx \cdot (y)(Gy \supset xSy) \supset Sx]$
$(x)(Gx \supset Px)$
$\overline{(x)[Fx \cdot (y)(Py \supset xSy) \supset Sx]}$

5 Do the following formulae compose a consistent set?

$$(x)(Px \supset Qx)$$
$$(x)(Sx \supset (\exists y)(Py \cdot \sim xRy))$$
$$(x)(y)(Sx \cdot Qy \supset yTx)$$
$$(\exists x)(\exists y)(Sx \cdot Py \cdot \sim xTy)$$
$$(x)(u)(v)(Pu \cdot Pv \cdot Sx \cdot uTx \supset xRv)$$

6 Use the technique of dequantification to prove that the following are logically necessary.

a. $(x)(Fx \supset Gx) \cdot (x)(Gx \supset Hx) \supset (x)(Fx \supset Hx)$
b. $(w)(u)(v)[(x)(y)(Sy \cdot xRy \supset Sx) \cdot Sw \cdot uRw \cdot vRu \supset Sv]$
c. If the uncles of musicians were always musicians, then the nephews of non-musicians could never be musicians.

7 Show the following to be logically necessary.

$$(\exists x)(y)(Fx \supset Fy \supset Gx \supset Gy)$$

8 Assume:
a. The class S is non-empty.
b. $(x)(y)[Sx \supset (xRy \equiv Ty)]$
c. $(x)[(\exists y)(xRy) \equiv Sx]$

Prove:
a. Some S is T.
b. Some S is R to some T.
c. Some T is R to itself.

9   Assume:

   a.   Every P is richer than someone.

   b.   Everyone poorer than someone is in S.

   c.   No S is poorer than any P.

   Prove:

   There are no P's.

10   Discuss the validity of the following arguments:

   a.   Some members of the International Bottle set can outdrink every member of the Rackets Club. Every member of the Goon Club is in the Rackets Club. All members of the International Bottle Set are on the license board. Therefore, some members of the license board can outdrink every member of the Goon Club.

   b.   Every member of the Athletics Club can outrun some man on the college team. The university team is contained within the athletic club. The college team is contained within the Varsity Club. Therefore, every man on the university team can outrun some man on the Varsity Club.

   c.   No man on the college squad can outplay any man on the university team. Every major in education is on the college squad. All members of the Athletics Club are on the university team. Hence, no major in education can outplay any member of the Athletics Club.

   d.   Every member of S is a parent of at least one female child. Every member of U is a brother of some member of S. Therefore, every member of U is an uncle of at least one female child.

11   Prove that $(\exists x)(Fx \supset Gx)$ and $(x)(Fx) \supset (\exists x)(Gx)$ are logically equivalent.

12   Prove: $(x)(y)(Sy \cdot xRy \supset Sx) \equiv (x)(y)(\sim Sy \cdot yRx \supset \sim Sx)$

4

Invalidity

We have up to now been engaged in showing that various sorts of arguments are valid, and we have also noted from time to time that mere failure to prove validity does not amount to a proof of invalidity. We must now attempt to face up to the problems involved in any attempt to prove that a particular argument is invalid.

In the first place, we must remind ourselves that a valid argument is valid by virtue of some form or other. If we find a validating argument form, then it follows that any substitution instance of that form is valid. But an argument is not proved invalid merely because it is a substitution instance of a non-validating argument form. Thus every syllogism is a substitution instance of the non-validating argument form

A
B

C

Yet we know that syllogisms are valid, if they are substitution instances of validating forms of syllogistic argument; and we have learned how to determine whether or not a syllogistic form is a validating argument form. But a particular argument may be valid even though it is a substitution instance of a non-validating syllogistic form.

For example, the argument form

ALL S IS M.
SOME Q IS M.

SOME Q IS S.

is a non-validating syllogistic form. Still, it is possible to construct a substitution instance of this form which will, in fact, be valid: not valid by virtue of this form, to be sure, but still valid. E.g.,

I
ALL WRITERS ARE SENSITIVE.
SOME POETS ARE SENSITIVE.

SOME POETS ARE WRITERS.

To see that this argument is valid, we note, first, that the statement "Every poet is a writer" is a necessary statement. Its denial is inconsistent. For by a poet we mean here a writer of a special sort. Second, it is a consequence of the second premiss that there are poets. By the Adjunctive Principle and the Implicative Principle, it follows from these two statements that some poets are writers. The premiss, "All writers are sensitive", makes no contribution to the argument whatsoever. Hence, the argument is seen to be a valid argument, despite the fact that it is a substitution instance of a non-validating syllogistic form.

Now, it may be objected that I is, strictly, invalid, that it is in fact an enthymeme, and that, strictly speaking, the valid argument is

II
ALL WRITERS ARE SENSITIVE.
SOME POETS ARE SENSITIVE.
EVERY POET IS A WRITER.

SOME POETS ARE WRITERS.

But if argument II is valid and "Every poet is a writer" is a necessary truth, as we claim, then I must be valid also. For a necessary premiss is redundant. Let us see why.

Suppose

III
A_1
.
.
.
A_n
$\overline{B}$

is a valid argument and that A_1 is a necessary truth. Then $\sim A_1$ is inconsistent. This means, we remember, that from $\sim A_1$ an omniparent statement is derivable.

Since III is, by hypothesis, valid, the C-set of III must be inconsistent. That is, the set $[A_1, A_2, \ldots, A_n, \sim B]$ must be an inconsistent set. It follows that the argument

IV
A_2
.
.
.
A_n
$\sim B$
$\overline{\sim A_1}$

is valid. For the C-set of IV is equivalent to the C-set of III, which, we know, is an inconsistent set. Since $\sim A_1$ is inconsistent, the premisses of IV must be an inconsistent set. That is, $[A_2, \ldots, A_n, \sim B]$ is an inconsistent set. But this last set is the C-set of the argument

V
A_2
.
.
.
A_n
$\overline{B}$

The argument V must then be valid, for its C-set is inconsistent.

Hence, A_1 must be redundant. For if III is valid, V also must be valid. It follows that if II is valid, I also must be valid, provided that "Every poet is a writer" is a statement which is necessarily true. But how do we ascertain that "Every poet is a writer" is necessarily true? The answer is that here we must appeal to the meaning of the word "poet", which is expressed in some such definition as "A poet is a writer of verse".

Of course, the word "poet" sometimes is used to communicate a different meaning, e.g., the concept of a person endowed with exceptional sensibility. But if we utilized *that* meaning, we should be considering an altogether different argument. In order to determine the validity of an argument, we must first determine what the argument is, and this involves fixing the meanings of the symbols which occur therein, in case such meanings are relevant. "The same argument" signifies not only sameness of shape but also sameness of sense or meaning. Therefore, if we modify the sense of "poet" in argument I, we no longer have the same argument. It is, admittedly, not the concern of the logician whether the argument of a historical person should be construed in this way or that. That is a problem of history and linguistics. The logical problem is: Is an argument, interpreted in a certain manner, valid, whether such interpretation is historically correct or not?

Our problem is how to prove the invalidity of arguments. We have seen that we do not prove an argument invalid by our subjective failure to prove it valid. Nor do we prove it invalid by showing that it is a substitution instance of a non-validating form of argument.

Those who like fruit like apples. Some men do not like fruit. Therefore, some men do not like apples.

may usefully be compared with:

All cats are animals. Some dogs are not cats. Therefore, some dogs are not animals.

Both arguments are substitution instances of the non-validating form

ALL L IS A.
SOME M IS NOT L.
———————————
SOME M IS NOT A.

Yet the first argument is valid and the second invalid. The reason is that in the first argument the conclusion is subaltern to the minor premiss. This fact is established by an analysis of the meanings of the phrases, "those who like fruit" and "those who like apples".

We know that an argument is invalid just in case its C-set is consistent. Our problem is, therefore, the problem of determining the consistency of a set of statements.

Now, a set of statements is consistent just in case it is logically possible for there to be a system of objects satisfying those statements. It is not requisite that there should actually exist such a system of objects, but only that such a system should be logically possible. We shall attempt to explain this idea in more precise language.

Let B be a set of totally singular statements and, moreover, let B be a consistent set. We wish to construct another set of statements, K, according to certain rules, which we shall presently specify, so that K too will be consistent. The rules of valid argument are rules for transforming a set of premises into a set of conclusions so that if the premises are true the conclusions must also be true. We say, therefore, that the rules of inference are truth-preserving. What we are now engaged in is the task of formulating rules which are consistency-preserving. These rules enable us to transform a consistent B into a consistent K. We provide no method for determining whether B is a consistent set of statements. But if we know or assume that B is consistent, we shall be able to infer that K also is consistent and, therefore, that any subclass of K must be consistent.

Suppose that A is a set of sentences which are totally singular in form and let $[a, b, c, \ldots]$ be the complete list of individual constants occurring in the sentences of A. We call this set of individual constants the class U and we shall restrict our discussion to the case in which U is a finite class. These individual constants need not be names of actual things. It will suffice for our purpose if they be taken as arbitrary constants in the sense of the previous chapter. Let the number of arbitrary constants in U be i.

We shall, in what follows, use the expression $E(n)$ to designate a formula which contains the unquantified individual variable "n", and which contains no other unquantified variable.

By a U-value of $E(n)$, we mean the result of substituting a constant in U for "n" in $E(n)$.

A set K is said to be *based* on A if and only if k satisfies the following conditions:

1. The set A is contained within K.
2. Anything derivable from A is in K.
3. If some U-value of $E(n)$ is in K, then $(\exists n)(E(n))$ is in K, however $E(n)$ be chosen.
4. If every U-value of $E(n)$ is in K, then $(n)(E(n))$ is in K, however $E(n)$ be chosen.
5. Nothing is in K unless its being so follows from these rules.

It is here presupposed that A is a finite set of statements and that the class U contains the i arbitrary constants occurring in the singular sentences of A and that no other individual constants occur in A.

The Consistency Principle

The Consistency Principle is as follows: If A is a consistent set of singular statements such as we have described and K is based upon A, then any subset of K is consistent. The intuition behind this principle is that if it is logically possible that a system of i objects satisfies a set of statements, then that set of statements must be a consistent set.

We shall discuss a series of applications of this consistency principle.

APPLICATION I. To prove that the following argument is invalid.

ALL S IS P.   ALL DOGS ARE ANIMALS.

NO Q IS S.   NO SQUIRREL IS A DOG.

SOME Q IS NOT P.   SOME SQUIRRELS ARE NOT ANIMALS.

We know that this argument is invalid if its C-set is consistent. The C-set is [All S is P, No Q is S, All Q is P]. We take as our A-set the set [$S(a)$, $P(a)$]. In this case, U consists of a single constant, viz., a. That the set [$S(a)$, $P(a)$] is consistent we do not prove. We recognize that it is consistent. By the consistency principle we can, however, prove the consistency of the C-set of the argument.

From the A-set we derive, by the Fundamental Principle, the sentences

$$Sa \supset Pa, \qquad Qa \supset Sa, \qquad \text{and} \qquad Qa \supset Pa$$

These sentences are, therefore, in K. Consider now the formulae

$$Sx \supset Px, \qquad Qx \supset Sx, \qquad \text{and} \qquad Qx \supset Px$$

We note that every U-value of each of these formulae is in K. Hence, by the rules for constructing K, the following statements are in K:

$$(x)(Sx \supset Px), \qquad (x)(Qx \supset Sx), \qquad \text{and} \qquad (x)(Qx \supset Px)$$

By the Consistency Principle, this set is consistent. But this set is the C-set of the original argument. That argument, therefore, must be invalid.

To show that an argument is invalid, we construct an A-set whose consistency is known. Then we must construct a K-set based on A containing the C-set as a subclass. If we can do so, we shall prove the argument to be invalid. On the other hand, mere failure to accomplish this proves nothing.

APPLICATION II

Every human being is deceived by some human being or other.
Therefore, some human being is deceived by every human being.

This argument is evidently invalid, but we do not need to leave this claim unsubstantiated. The C-set of this argument is

$$[(x)(Hx \supset (\exists y)(Hy \cdot yDx)), \quad (y)(Hy \supset (\exists x)(Hx \cdot \sim yDx))]$$

Let us take as our U-set the set of constants x_0, y_0, z_0. Our A-set is

$$Hx_0, \ Hy_0, \ Hz_0$$
$$y_0Dx_0, \ z_0Dy_0, \ x_0Dz_0$$
$$\sim y_0Dz_0, \ \sim x_0Dy_0, \ \sim z_0Dx_0$$

By the rules of K-set construction, we verify that every U-value of $(\exists y)(Hy \cdot yDx)$ is in K. Therefore, every U-value of $Hx \supset (\exists y)(Hy \cdot yDx)$ is in K. In the same way, we verify that every U-value of $Hy \supset (\exists x)(Hx \cdot \sim yDx)$ is in K. The C-set of the argument is, therefore, in K. Since the C-set is thus shown by the Consistency Principle to be consistent, the original argument must of course be invalid.

A few comments about the Consistency Principle are now in order. As we pointed out, the principle tells us that if sentences of a certain kind form a consistent set, then certain other sentences form a consistent set. If a certain A-set is consistent, so must a certain K-set be consistent. That the A-sets in the preceding illustrations are consistent, we cannot prove, however. It is here a question simply of recognizing consistency in simple cases. The meanings which we have assigned to "human" and "deceive" are such that it is logically possible for there to be a universe consisting of three elements satisfying the requirements listed in the A-set. It is then provable that the argument is invalid. If it should be argued that, from the point of view of linguistics, we are misinterpreting the sense of the argument, our answer is that this may perhaps be so. This controverts no claim which we have made. We make only the hypothetical affirmation, that if certain meanings are assigned to the symbols, then we recognize the consistency of an A-set of singular sentences, and we can prove the validity of the argument as we have interpreted it.

EXERCISES

Show the following to be invalid arguments. In your exposition, make clear what your interpretation is of the sense of the predicates which occur in the arguments, if that is needed to make your discussion conclusive.

1   ALL CROWS CAW.

    NO NIGHTINGALE IS A CROW.
    _____

    NO NIGHTINGALE CAWS.

2   ALL INVENTORS ARE PRACTICAL.

    SOME INVENTORS ARE NOT ENGINEERS.
    _____

    SOME ENGINEERS ARE NOT PRACTICAL.

3   EVERY CAMEL IS LARGER THAN EVERY DOG.

    ALL CAMELS HAVE HUMPED BACKS.
    _____

    EVERY HUMPBACKED ANIMAL IS LARGER THAN EVERY DOG.

PART 2

Inconclusive
Argument

5

Probability

1. If we perform an experiment, there will, in general, be a set of possible outcomes of that experiment. Which of these possible outcomes will be realized we may not be able to predict with perfect confidence. Yet we may be able to determine their probabilities. For example, if our experiment consists of flipping a standard coin in the usual way, we are confident that the coin will not fall on edge, but we do not know on which side the coin will elect to fall. Nevertheless, we believe that we know the probability that the coin will fall heads. Also, if our experiment consists of flipping the coin one hundred times, we should freely admit our ignorance as to the precise number of times that heads will appear. But that the number of heads will occur somewhere in the interval between thirty and seventy is an experimental outcome whose probability is extremely high.

Again, suppose that our experiment consists in selecting at random five cards from a poker deck. We are quite ignorant, because of the very definition of the experiment, of its outcome. But we can calculate the probability of obtaining a royal flush on the basis of quite plausible assumptions and can, accordingly, state that it is unreasonable to expect this particular outcome. (The probability of obtaining a royal flush by chance is 1/649,740.)

There is no need to stress what is, after all, quite obvious. Rational expectation concerning the outcome of a particular experiment does not necessarily mean that we can predict with certainty any particular experimental outcome. But it does signify that we are able to estimate correctly the probabilities of such outcomes.

If logic is the general theory of argument, then probability is one of the topics which logic must discuss. For, as we have pointed out, there are many arguments which do not purport to be valid in the sense of deductive logic but which have, nevertheless, varying degrees of conclusiveness. The cogency of this kind of argument can be analyzed with the help of probability theory, and this is the primary reason for our entering upon the following discussion.

1. Suppose our experiment is to select at random a single card from a deck of bridge cards which have been properly shuffled. We shall, for the time being, take for granted the idea of random selection and shuffling. We may then ask for the probability that the card to be selected from the deck has a certain property. For example, we may ask for the probability that the card selected will be either an ace or a deuce, and we would, undoubtedly accept the answer $\frac{2}{13}$ as correct. It is essential to keep in mind that $\frac{2}{13}$ is the correct answer in relation to the assumption that the method of selection is random.

Instead of saying that $\frac{2}{13}$ is the probability that the card selected by the method M is either an ace or deuce, we shall often say: given the deck and the method of selection, the probability of the property, ace or deuce, is $\frac{2}{13}$. We may now express the matter in a more general way. Let G be a set of alternatives and M a method of selection which, when applied to G, yields a definite selection of an element of G. Then, in respect to the system which consists of M and G, there is a definite probability that an element selected from G has a certain property, F. In other words, the property F has a definite probability in respect to the system $[G, M]$. This is expressed by writing

$$\text{Prob } (G, M, F) = q$$

where q is a non-negative real number belonging to the interval from zero to one. Whenever the context makes it clear what G and M are, we shall write

$$\text{Prob } (F) = q$$

To sum up: we interpret an experiment as a well-defined operation of the kind M, by which an element is selected from a finite set of alternatives, G. To say that the probability of the property F is q is the same as saying that F has this probability in respect to the system $[G, M]$. And we interpret this as meaning that the probability is q that the alternative selected from G has the character F.

2. The set of alternatives, G, may be any well-defined, finite, non-empty set. In some problems, G may be a set of individual concrete things. For example, our problem might be to determine the probability that a marble selected from a bag has a certain color. In this case, the method of selection may consist of picking out a ball "at random".

But the set G need not consist of concrete individuals. It may consist of abstract properties. For example, G may be a set consisting of the two properties, Heads and Tails. The method of selection, M, may consist of flipping a standard coin in the usual way (we can, after all, teach people how to flip coins). If the coin falls heads, the property Heads is selected. If the coin falls tails, the property Tails is selected. If the coin falls on edge, the experiment doesn't count and the experiment must be repeated. Given this set of alternatives and this method of selection, we may then speak of the probability that an element selected from G will have a certain property.

It is quite clear that the probability of a property is affected by the method of selection as well as by the characteristics of the alternatives of G. E.g., suppose that G consists of small metal balls and that half of them are made of silver and that half are made of iron. One might be tempted to say that the probability is one-half that a selected member of G is iron. But now suppose the method of selection was to use a magnet just strong enough to raise one iron ball. In this case the probability of silver would be zero. The probability of a property is relative to a method of selection as well as to a class of alternatives, and unless these are specified, or are specifiable on demand, we attach no sense to the expression "Prob $(F) = q$".

3. The properties which are significantly ascribable (truly or falsely ascribable) to the alternatives of G form a set which we call the property class of G. The reader will note that probabilities are literally ascribed not to the elements of G but to the properties in the property class of G. Important for our purpose is a certain subclass of the property class of G. This subclass we call the iota class of G.

If a is any object, then the property of being identical with a is an iota property. Those iota properties in the property class of G compose the iota class of G. We use the symbol, ιa, to designate the iota property belonging to a, i.e., the property of being identical with a. The reader will note that if a is not an element of G, its iota property may still be in the iota class of G. For it may be meaningful (though false) to ascribe such a property to a member of G.

We are now able to formulate the rules for reckoning probabilities.

4. Let $x_1, x_2, \ldots, x_m$ be the complete list of elements in G. Then, if we call the probability of an iota property of a member of G an iota probability, we may say that the sum of the iota probabilities of the elements of G equals unity. This requirement is analytically involved in the very meaning of probability.

5. Let F be any non-empty property in the property set of G and let $x_1, x_2, \ldots, x_i$ be the complete list of the instances of F in G. Then

$$\text{Prob } (F) = \text{Prob } (\iota x_1) + \text{Prob } (\iota x_2) + \cdots + \text{Prob } (\iota x_i)$$

We shall call the iota probabilities of the instances of F the iota probabilities under F. Then our present rule may be paraphrased as: the probability of any non-empty property is the sum of the iota probabilities under it. We further stipulate that if F has no instances in G, then the probability of F is zero. However, if the probability of F is zero, it does not necessarily follow that F has no instances in G.

The preceding rules do not enable us to determine what the probabilities of the various properties in the property set of G are. They state only certain logically necessary and formal conditions with which our probability estimates must comply. Any system of probability estimates which do not comply with these requirements is inconsistent or illogical. Nevertheless, we must emphasize that the logical consistency of our probability estimates does not guarantee that those probability estimates are materially correct.

We may illustrate by a simple example. Let our set of alternatives, G, consists of a red and a black ball. The method of selection consists of shuffling and then picking one of the balls with one's eyes blindfolded. What is the probability of red? The answer is surely not one which can be guaranteed by logic or mathematics. It is experience which persuades us that these probabilities are equal. A universe can be imagined in which our hands would be attracted to the red. Such a possibility is not eliminated by mathematics. But observation convinces us that if we were to conduct such experiments a large number of times, red and black would occur with very nearly the same frequency. It is this somewhat vague expectation of approximately equal frequencies which justifies the assignment of equal probabilities to red and black in the present example. We shall return to this point later.

6. If F_1 and F_2 are mutually exclusive in G (i.e., nothing in G has both properties), then

$$\text{Prob } (F_1) + \text{Prob } (F_2) = \text{Prob } (F_1 \vee F_2)$$

The items in G having the property $F_1 \vee F_2$ are the items of F_1 in G together with the items of F_2 in G. The probability of $F_1 \vee F_2$ is then obtained by adding the probabilities of the iota properties of its instances. This is equivalent to taking the sum of the probabilities of the iota properties of the instances of F_1 added to the sum of the iota properties of the instances of F_2.

7. The probability of $- F$ equals 1 minus the probability of F. This follows from 6. Since F and $- F$ are exclusive, the probability of $F \vee - F$ is the same as the probability of F added to the probability of $- F$. But the probability of $F \vee - F$

is unity. Hence we have

$$\text{Prob } (F) + \text{Prob } (- F) = 1$$

8. $\text{Prob } (F_1) + \text{Prob } (F_2) - \text{Prob } (F_1 \cdot F_2) = \text{Prob } (F_1 \vee F_2)$

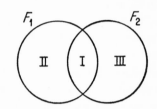

FIGURE 17

We represent $F_1 \cdot F_2$ by I; $F_1 \cdot - F_2$ by II; $F_2 \cdot - F_1$ by III. By 6, we have:

$$\text{Prob (II)} + \text{Prob (I)} = \text{Prob } (F_1)$$

which is to say:

$$\text{Prob (II)} = \text{Prob } (F_1) - \text{Prob (I)}$$

Also by 6,

$$\text{Prob (II)} + \text{Prob } (F_2) = \text{Prob (II} \vee F_2) = \text{Prob } (F_1 \vee F_2)$$

By substitution,

$$\text{Prob } (F_1) - \text{Prob (I)} + \text{Prob } (F_2) = \text{Prob } (F_1 \vee F_2)$$

which is equivalent to 8.

As a typographic convenience, we shall hereafter write "P(F)" in place of "Prob (F)".

9. We use the symbol "P(F, H)", to be read as "the conditional probability from F to H", to mean the probability that an object selected from G is an instance of H, given the assumption that it is an instance of F. In other words, P(F, H) is the probability that an object selected from among the F's in G is an H. We adopt the definition

$$P(F, H) = \frac{P(F \cdot H)}{P(F)}$$

with the proviso that $P(F) \neq 0$. If $P(F) = 0$, then the expression "P(F, H)" is undefined or meaningless.

Given that neither $P(F)$ nor $P(H)$ is zero, we have

$$P(F \cdot H) = P(F) \times P(F, H)$$
$$P(H \cdot F) = P(F \cdot H) = P(H) \times P(H, F)$$

Therefore,

(1) $$P(F, H) = \frac{P(H) \times P(H, F)}{P(F)}$$

We may illustrate the use of (1) by a simple example. Let G be a large heap of keys of various sizes, makes and materials. On the basis of a number of trials, we estimate the probability to be $\frac{1}{3}$ that a key arbitrarily selected will fit a certain lock. The probability of selecting a brass key is estimated to be $\frac{1}{5}$. And the probability that a brass key so selected will fit the lock is estimated to be $\frac{2}{3}$. What shall be our estimate of the probability that if a key fits the lock, it is made of brass?

Using (1), let "F" denote the property of fitting the lock and let "H" denote the property, brass. We have, accordingly,

$$P(F, H) = \frac{\frac{1}{5} \times \frac{2}{3}}{\frac{1}{3}} = \frac{2}{5}$$

SUMMARY

We cannot determine by logic alone the probability of any property. Mathematics is the art of drawing consequences from our assumptions. The verification of those assumptions depends upon observation. However, whatever the correct probability estimates may turn out to be, they must satisfy the formal, mathematical requirements of probability theory which represent a necessary though not sufficient condition for the correctness of our probability estimates.

We have indicated that probability is relative to a *kind* of experiment or operation, to a *method* of selection. It is not necessary that anyone should actually have flipped any coins in order for the probability of heads to be $\frac{1}{2}$, although it may be necessary to flip coins in order to verify some particular estimate of the probability. One may construe the probability of heads as a *disposition* for coins to fall heads about half the time in a long series of trials. This is a purposely vague statement which one clarifies as one learns how to reckon probabilities and also how to confirm and disconfirm probability estimates by reference to observation.

EXERCISES

1   If one draws a card at random from a bridge deck, what is the probability that it is a black jack? The notion of randomness implies that all iota properties are equally likely in respect to the method of selection. Hence, the probability of being the jack of clubs is equal to the probability of being the jack of spades, or $\frac{1}{52}$. The property of being a black jack is the property of being the jack of clubs *or* being the jack of spades. Hence, the probability of being a black jack is $\frac{1}{52}$ plus $\frac{1}{52}$, or $\frac{1}{26}$.

2   If one draws a card at random from a bridge deck, what is the conditional probability that if it is black then it is a jack?

$$P(B, J) = \frac{P(B \cdot J)}{P(B)} = \frac{\frac{1}{26}}{\frac{1}{2}} = \frac{1}{13}$$

This calculation depends on the definition of conditional probability. The numerator was calculated, in the preceding example, as $\frac{1}{26}$. The denominator is calculated by the use of the rule that the probability of a property is the sum of the iota probabilities under it. Here there are 26 such iota properties, each with probability $\frac{1}{52}$. One notices that if one drew from the black cards of the deck, the probability of obtaining a jack is also $\frac{1}{13}$. This illustrates the meaning of conditional probability.

3   If one selects a card at random, what is the probability that it is neither a queen nor an even-numbered card?

The probability that the card selected is even-numbered is the probability that it is a deuce, or a four, or a six, or an eight, or a ten is $5 \times \frac{1}{13}$.

The probability that it is a queen is $\frac{1}{13}$.

The probability that it is either even or a queen is $\frac{6}{13}$.

The probability that it is *neither* a queen *nor* even is $1 - \frac{6}{13}$, or $\frac{7}{13}$.

2. A *permutation* is a sequence or arrangement of elements. A *combination* is a set of elements. Combination x and combination y are identical if and only if they possess the same elements. But permutations must be distinguished, even if they possess the same elements, provided that the elements are differently arranged. Thus, (a, b) and (b, a) are different permutations. The size of a combination refers to the number of distinct elements therein. The size of a permutation refers to the number of positions in the sequence. E.g., (a, a, a) is of size 3, though it has only one element.

TWO RULES OF ELEMENTARY ARITHMETIC

1. If X is a class consisting of m mutually exclusive sets each containing n elements, then there are $m \times n$ elements distributed through the m sets of X.

2. If $X_1, X_2, \ldots, X_m$ are sets whose numbers of elements are $x_1, x_2, \ldots, x_m$, respectively, and these sets are not necessarily mutually exclusive or distinct, then the number of permutations, of size m, of the form

$$a_1, a_2, \ldots, a_m$$

where a_1 is a member of the set X_1, a_2 is a member of X_2, $\ldots$, etc., is the product of the numbers

$$x_1, x_2, \ldots, x_m$$

It should be noted that these permutations may contain repetitions. However, if the sets $X_1, \ldots, X_m$ are mutually exclusive, then the number of constructible permutations coincides with the number of constructible combinations.

EXERCISES

1 In how many ways can truth values be assigned to the letters p, q, and r?

   We choose X_1, X_2, and X_3 so that they are identical with one another and with the set of truth values, (T, F). The number of permutations (a_1, a_2, a_3) so that a_1 is in X_1, a_2 is in X_2, and a_3 is in X_3 is, therefore, $2 \times 2 \times 2$.

2 There are four ways of going from A to B and six ways of going from B to C. In how many ways can one go from A to C via B?

   We wish to designate the number of permutations (x, y) so that x is a path from A to B and y is a path from B to C. This number is 4×6.

We use the symbol "$_nP_r$" to designate the number of permutations of n things taken r at a time, where no repetition is allowed to occur in any of the permutations counted, and where r is not, of course, greater than n.

It is evident that $_nP_1 = 1$.

We wish to show that $_nP_2 = n(n - 1)$. That is, given any class, X, consisting of the distinct elements x_1, x_2, $\ldots$, x_n, we wish to show that the number of permutations of size 2, constructible out of these elements, is $n(n - 1)$, each permutation consisting of distinct elements. To show this, we sort all of the permutations of size 2 into n exclusive classes, X_1, $\ldots$, X_n. The class X_1 consists of all ordered pairs of elements of X whose first element is x_1. The class X_2 consists of all ordered pairs whose first element is x_2. And so on to X_n, which consists of all ordered pairs whose first element is x_n. It is clear that each of the sets X_1, $\ldots$, X_n must contain $n - 1$ ordered pairs. There are, therefore, $n(n - 1)$ ordered pairs distributed through the classes X_1, $\ldots$, X_n.

To prove that $_nP_3 = n(n - 1)(n - 2)$, we proceed similarly. Given a class X consisting of x_1, $\ldots$, x_n, we wish to show that the number of permutations of size 3 constructible out of these elements is $n(n - 1)(n - 2)$, where no permutation contains repetition of any element. To begin with, we sort all of the ordered triples into exclusive classes, X_1, $\ldots$, $X_{n(n-1)}$. We have seen in the preceding paragraph that $_nP_2$ is $n(n - 1)$. We may arrange all of the ordered *pairs* in sequence so that we may speak of the first ordered pair, the second ordered pair, $\ldots$, the last ordered pair. Then X_1 is the class of ordered triples each of which begins with the first ordered pair. X_2 is the class of ordered triples each of which begins with the second ordered pair. And so on to $X_{(n)(n-1)}$, which consists of all of the ordered triples beginning with the last ordered pair. It is evident, since repetitions are not allowable, that there are $n - 2$ ordered triples in each of the classes, X_1, $\ldots$, $X_{n(n-1)}$. Hence, there must be $n(n - 1)(n - 2)$ ordered triples distributed through the $n(n - 1)$ classes.

We may, in the same manner, show for any r not greater than n,

$$_nP_r = n(n - 1)(n - 2) \ldots \text{to } r \text{ factors.}$$

The rth factor is $n - (r - 1)$, so we may write

$$_nP_r = n(n - 1)(n - 2) \ldots (n - r + 1)$$

The symbol $r!$ is used to designate the product

$$r(r - 1) \ldots 1$$

Hence, $_nP_n = n(n - 1)(n - 2) \ldots 1 = n!$

It is customary to stipulate that $0! = 1$. Then, for every r not greater than n,

$$_nP_r = \frac{n(n - 1)(n - 2) \ldots (n - r + 1)(n - r)!}{(n - r)!} = \frac{n!}{(n - r)!}$$

We use the symbol "$_nC_r$" to designate the number of combinations of n things taken r at a time. We wish to calculate the value of this function for any positive value of n and for any value of r not greater than n. Let X be any set consisting of n elements. The number of permutations of size r which can be formed from the elements of X, we have seen, is $n!/(n - r)!$, it being given that none of these permutations contains repetition of the same element. These $n!/(n - r)!$ permutations of size r can be sorted into classes, $K_1, K_2, \ldots, K_L$, in accordance with the following principle: if two permutations possess the same elements they belong to the same K-class; otherwise they belong to different K-classes. In other words, different permutations belonging to the same K-class are permutations of the same elements of X. Hence, the number of K-classes, L, is the number of combinations of size r selected from X. Now the number of permutations within any of the K-classes is $_rP_r$ or $r!$. Hence, L multiplied by $r!$ yields the total number of permutations distributed through the K-classes. Accordingly, we have $L \cdot r! = {}_nP_r$, or

$$_nC_r = \frac{n!}{(n - r)! \times r!} = \frac{_nP_r}{r!}$$

EXERCISES

1   $_6P_2 = 6 \times 5 = 30$

2   $_4C_3 = \dfrac{4 \times 3 \times 2}{3 \times 2 \times 1} = 4$

3   Prove that $_nC_r = {}_nC_{n-r}$.

4   If F, G, and H are mutually exclusive classes and F contains three elements, G contains four elements, and H contains two elements, then how many combinations of six things can be formed from the elements of F, G, and H such that, in each combination, two are selected from each class?

$$_3C_2 = 3 \qquad {}_4C_2 = 6 \qquad {}_2C_2 = 1$$

Therefore, the number of permissible combinations equals 6 × 3 × 1, or 18.

3. A method of selection may be applied repeatedly to a class of alternatives, G, to form a sample of G. We may then discuss the probability that a sample so formed has a certain property. If the order in which the elements are selected is irrelevant, we identify the sample with a combination of elements. If the order is relevant, we identify it with a permutation of elements. Hence, we shall speak of a combination sample or a permutation sample, depending upon the problem which engages our interest. If, in generating a sample, we replace the item previously selected before drawing the next item, we are said to sample with replacement. Otherwise, we are said to sample without replacement. If we sample without replacement, our sample will contain no repetitions, and its size cannot exceed the number of elements of G. If we sample with replacement, however, there may be repetitions and our sample will be a permutation whose size may exceed the size of G. In discussing the probability that a sample has a certain property, it is necessary to specify what the system of alternatives is and what method of selection is being referred to. E.g., if we ask what is the probability of drawing a sequence of certain cards from a deck, we must be clear as to whether the cards are drawn with or without replacement, and whether the order in which they are drawn is relevant to the question which we seek to answer.

Suppose that we sample without replacement from a set of n elements. We wish to determine the probability that a combination sample of size r has a certain property, F. Here our set of alternatives consists of all possible combination samples drawn from G of size r. The number of such combinations is $n!/(n-r)!r!$. The iota properties of these combinations are assigned probabilities so that their sum is unity. Any other non-empty property in the property class of this set of alternatives has for its probability the sum of the iota probabilities under it.

If, still sampling without replacement, our alternatives are permutation samples of size r, then the number of alternatives would be $n!/(n-r)!$ However, if we sample with replacement, then the number of permutation samples of size r must be n^r.

As we have already emphasized, we cannot by logic or pure mathematics alone evaluate the probabilities of the properties of our alternatives. For this purpose we require empirical data whose credentials cannot be certified by mathematics alone.

Randomness

A method of selection, M, is random with respect to a class of alternatives, G, just in case all of the iota probabilities of G are equal.

For example, if our alternatives are the 52 cards in a poker deck and our method of selection consists of shuffling the cards in an approved way and drawing a card, without peeking, from the complete deck, then we are persuaded by experience that each card tends to be drawn with approximately the same relative frequency as any other card. Hence, we represent the probability of each iota property as $\frac{1}{52}$. For example, the probability of the property, *being identical with the jack of spades*, is $\frac{1}{52}$.

It mus: be emphasized that the concept of randomness represents an ideal to which actual experiments approximate in varying degrees. For example, a perfect coin is not an actuality, presumably. But if we flip a dime many times heads and tails normally occur with approximately the same frequency, so that we are justified in regarding this method of selection as a random one. It is, of course, highly improbable, in a random sequence, that heads and tails will actually occur with *exactly* the same relative frequency in a sequence of experiments.

Of particular interest is the situation in which a sample of size r is produced at random by applying a method, M, r times to a finite set of alternatives. We may illustrate what is involved here by asking what is the probability that if one drew (without replacement) a pair of cards at random from a poker deck one would obtain a pair of kings.

One notes that in this example the set of alternatives is not the set of 52 cards but rather the totality of the combinations of size 2 selectable from the 52 cards. $_{52}C_2 = 1326$. Hence, the probability of obtaining any one of these combinations is $\frac{1}{1326}$. This follows from the hypothesis that the method of selecting combinations is random. Of these 1326 combinations, only six have the characteristic of being a pair of kings $(_4C_2 = 6)$. Hence, the desired probablility is the sum of the probabilities of the six favorable combinations. The correct answer is, then, $\frac{1}{221}$.

EXERCISES

1   If five cards are drawn without replacement and at random from a poker deck, what is the probability of drawing two pairs?

$1/_{52}C_5$ is the probability of *any* combination of five cards. We must find the number of such combination which have two pairs. These are the favorable combinations.

We begin by asking how many combinations contain a pair of kings, a pair of queens, and some other card.

There are six ways of selecting two kings out of four, six ways of selecting two queens out of four, and 44 ways of selecting the remaining card.

Hence, there are 36.44 ways of selecting a pair of kings and pair of queens. We may write down the list:

KQ   pair of kings, pair of queens and another card
KJ   pair of kings, pair of jacks and another card
K10   pair of kings, pair of tens and another card
  .   .
  .   .
  .   .

There are 36 × 44 ways of obtaining each combination in the list. How many rows in the list are there? There are as many rows as there are ways of selecting two face values out of the 13. Hence, there are $_{13}C_2$ rows in the list, or 78 rows. There are 1584 ways of obtaining each of the possibilities represented by a row, so there are 78 × 1584 ways of obtaining two pairs. There are, that is to say, 123,552 ways of obtaining two pairs. The probability of obtaining each one of these is $1/_{52}C_5$. Hence, the probability of obtaining any one of these is

$$\frac{123,552}{_{52}C_5} = \frac{198}{4165}$$

2   What is the probability of drawing a full house?
     We begin by asking how many ways there are of drawing three kings and two queens. There are four ways of selecting three kings out of four, and six ways of drawing two queens out of four. Since each trio of kings may be combined with any duo of queens, there are 24 ways of selecting three kings and two queens. Write down the list:

$$KQ \quad \text{3 kings and 2 queens}$$
$$KJ \quad \text{3 kings and 2 jacks}$$

. .
. .
. .

How many rows in the list are there? Here we have as many rows as there are *permutations* of 13 things taken two at a time or $13 \times 12 = 156$. We want the number of *permutations* here, for KQ and QK represent different combinations, namely three kings and two queens in the first instance and three queens and two kings in the second. Hence, there are $156 \times 24 = 3744$ ways of selecting a full house. Each of these selections has the probability $1/_{52}C_5$; the probability of obtaining any one of them is, consequently, $\frac{6}{4165}$. Therefore, it is thirty-three times more probable that two pairs will be selected than a full house.

Permutation Samples

One may characterize a permutation by saying that its ith term has a certain property. We therefore adopt the notation "F^i" to designate the property which a sequence has just in case the property F is situated in the ith position.
     If s is the sequence $(x_1, \ldots, x_m)$, then is is the property of being identical with s. Now, a sequence of size m has the property ιs just in case it possesses each of the properties

$$(\iota x_1)^1, \ (\iota x_2)^2, \ \ldots, \ (\iota x_m)^m$$

We saw earlier that the following rule holds:

$$P(F \cdot H) = P(F) \times P(F, H) [(P(F) \neq 0)]$$

A particular case of this rule is

$$P(F^i \cdot H^j) = P(F^i) \times P(F^i, H^j)$$

This rule says, in effect, that if our system of alternatives consists of permutations of size m, the probability of having F in the ith place and H in the jth place is equal to the probability of having F in the ith place multiplied by the conditional probability that H occurs in the jth place in case F is at the ith place.

We say that the properties F and H are independent just in case

$$P(F, H) = P(H)$$

or, equivalently, just in case

$$P(F \cdot H) = P(F) \times P(H)$$

More generally, the properties $F_1, \ldots, F_k$ are independent just in case

$$P(F_1 \cdot F_2 \cdot \cdots \cdot F_k) = P(F_1) \times P(F_2) \ldots P(F_k)$$

Bernoulli Sequences

If we flipped a coin 100 times, experience would indicate that these trials are independent of one another and that the probability of heads on any given trial is unaffected by the results of the other trials. Such a method of selection is called a Bernoulli method of selection, and any sequence generated by a Bernoulli method is called a Bernoulli sequence. Indeed, the example is typical except that coin flipping is a random operation if a symmetrical coin is used. But Bernoulli sequences need not consist of random events in the sense previously explained. If we flipped a biased coin a hundred times, the sequence might consist of independent events, but the probability of heads on a single trial need not be $\frac{1}{2}$.

Let the alternatives in G be divided into two classes which are exhaustive and exclusive, called successes and failures. Then a Bernoulli method of selection may be defined by the condition that the probability of obtaining exactly r successes in n successive applications of the method is $_nC_r p^r q^{n-r}$, where

p is the probability of an individual success and q is $1 - p$. $_nC_r$ is the number of sequences of size n which contain r successes. The probability of obtaining each particular one of these sequences is, by virtue of the independence of the trials $p^r q^{n-r}$.

EXERCISES

1   How many permutations can be formed of length 4 out of the two letters a and b, if there are to be as many a's as b's in each permutation?

This is the same as asking in how many ways can we select two things out of four and designate them as a. The answer is $_4C_2$.

2   What is the probability of obtaining two, three, or four heads in a sequence of six throws of a coin? Assume the method of selection to be Bernoullian and the coin fair.

THE MOST PROBABLE VALUE

For what value or values of r does $_nC_r p^r q^{n-r}$ have its greatest value? As r varies from 0 to n, $_nC_r p^r q^{n-r}$ increases to its greatest value or values and then decreases. We wish to determine for what values of r the double inequality holds:

$$_nC_{r-1} p^{r-1} q^{n-r+1} \leqslant {}_nC_r p^r q^{n-r} \geqslant {}_nC_{r+1} p^{r+1} q^{n-r-1}$$

I.e.,

$$\frac{n!}{(n - r + 1)!(r - 1)!} p^{r-1} q^{n-r+1} \leqslant \frac{n!}{(n - r)!r!} p^r q^{n-r}$$

$$\geqslant \frac{n!}{(r + 1)!(n - r - 1)!} p^{r+1} q^{n-r-1}$$

If we cancel out common factors we obtain

$$\frac{q^2}{(n - r + 1)(n - r)} \leqslant \frac{pq}{r(n - r)} \geqslant \frac{p^2}{r(r + 1)}$$

Therefore,

$$\frac{q}{n - r + 1} \leqslant \frac{p}{r}$$

$$rq \leqslant np - rp + p$$

Putting $1 - p$ for q gives

$$r \leqslant np + p$$

In the same way, we obtain

$$\frac{q}{n-r} \geqslant \frac{p}{r+1}$$

$$rq + q \geqslant np - rp$$

$$r - rp + 1 - p \geqslant np - rp$$

$$r \geqslant np + p - 1$$

$$r \geqslant np - q$$

Hence,

$$np - q \leqslant r \leqslant np + p$$

Hence, the most probable value of r must fall within the unit interval from $np - q$ to $np + p$. If np is an integer, it is the most probable value. If $np + p$ is an integer, then both it and $np - q$ are most probable values. Otherwise, whatever integer occurs in the interval $[np - q, np + p]$ is the most probable value. As an approximate way of speaking, np is often called the most probable value of r.

EXERCISE

1 How probable is it that, in a Bernoulli sequence of n trials, the most probable number of successes will be realized? For example, in a sequence of ten throws of a fair coin, how probable is it that we shall obtain exactly five heads?

The probability is

$$\frac{10!}{5! \cdot 5!} \left(\frac{1}{2}\right)^{10} = \frac{63}{256}$$

We see, therefore, that the most probable event is quite improbable. But the student can calculate that the alternatives to the most probable event are even more improbable.

The Binomial Theorem

From elementary algebra we have the identity

$$(p + q)^n = p^n + {}_nC_1 p^{n-1}q + {}_nC_2 p^{n-2}q^2 + \cdots + {}_nC_n q^n$$

Setting $p + q = 1$, we obtain

$$p^n + {}_nC_1 \cdot p^{n-1}q + {}_nC_2p^{n-2}q^2 + \cdots + {}_nC_nq^n = 1$$

or

$$\sum_{r=0}^{n} {}_nC_r \cdot p^r q^{n-r} = 1$$

THE EXPECTED VALUE OF r IN A BERNOULLI SEQUENCE OF n TRIALS

The expected value of the number of successes in a Bernoulli sequence of n trials is

$$\mathcal{E}(r) = \sum_{r=0}^{n} r \cdot {}_nC_r \cdot p^r q^{n-r}$$

Hence,

$$\mathcal{E}(r) = 0 \cdot {}_nC_0 \cdot p^0 q^n + 1 \cdot {}_nC_1 pq^{n-1} + \cdots + {}_nC_n p^n q^{n-n}$$
$$= npq^{n-1} + \cdots + p^n$$
$$= np(q + p)^{n-1} = np$$

Therefore, the expected value of r coincides with the most probable value.

THE EXPECTED VALUE OF r^2 IN A BERNOULLI SEQUENCE OF n TRIALS

$$\mathcal{E}(r^2) = \sum_{r=0}^{n} r^2 \cdot {}_nC_r p^r q^{n-r} = \sum_{r=0}^{n} r(r-1){}_nC_r p^r q^{n-r}$$

$$+ \sum_{r=0}^{n} r \cdot {}_nC_r p^r q^{n-r}$$

$$= \sum_{r=0}^{n} r(r-1){}_nC_r p^r q^{n-r} + np$$
$$= n(n-1)p^2$$
$$\times [q^{n-2} + (n-2)pq^{n-3} + \cdots + p^{n-2}] + np$$
$$= n(n-1)p^2[q+p]^{n-2} + np$$
$$= n(n-1)p^2 + np$$

THE VARIANCE OF r IN A BERNOULLI SEQUENCE OF n TRIALS

The variance in the possible number of successes in a Bernoulli sequence of n trials is defined as

$$\sum_{r=0}^{n} (np - r)^2 \cdot {}_nC_r p^r q^{n-r}$$

If we use the symbol σ^2 to denote the variance, then

$$\sigma^2 = n^2 p^2 \sum_{r=0}^{n} {}_nC_r p^r q^{n-r} - 2np \sum_{r=0}^{-n} r \cdot {}_nC_r p^r q^{n-r}$$

$$+ \sum_{r=0}^{n} r^2 {}_nC_r p^r q^{n-r}$$

$$= n^2 p^2 - 2n^2 p^2 + n(n-1)p^2 + np$$

$$= np - np^2 = np(1 - p) = npq$$

The square root of the variance, σ, is called the standard deviation.

We noted earlier that the probability is small of obtaining exactly the most probable number of successes. However, we are more apt to be interested in the probability of obtaining a number of successes which deviates from the expected number by more than a specified amount. In particular, we now raise the problem: what is the probability that the number of successes in a Bernoulli sequence of size n deviates from the most probable value by an amount exceeding $\lambda \cdot \sigma$? Here λ is a positive number and σ^2 is the quantity npq. We will show that the probability must be less than $1/\lambda^2$. In other words, the probability that r will deviate from np by an amount greater than two standard deviations will be shown to be less than $\frac{1}{4}$. The probability that r will deviate from np by an amount greater than three standard deviations will be shown to be less than $\frac{1}{9}, \ldots$, etc.

To establish this result, we need to consider three cases.

Case a: $p = 0$, $q = 1$.

The probability of obtaining a number of successes differing from the most probable number np by an amount exceeding $\lambda\sigma$ is, in this case, the probability of obtaining a number of

successes differing from 0 by a positive amount. And this is
the probability of obtaining either one success or two successes
or three successes or ... or n successes, which has the value
zero, since p, the probability of an individual success, is zero.
Therefore, when $p = 0$, the probability of obtaining a number
of successes differing from np by a positive amount must be
less than $1/\lambda^2$.

Case b: $p = 1$, $q = 0$.

The probability of obtaining a number of successes differing
from the most probable number, np, by an amount exceeding $\lambda\sigma$
is, in this case, the probability of obtaining a number of successes differing from n by an amount exceeding 0. This is the
probability of obtaining either one failure or two failures or
three failures, or ... or n failures, which has the value zero,
since q, the probability of an individual failure, is zero. Consequently, when $p = 1$ and $q = 0$, the probability is zero and
so less than $1/\lambda^2$ that one will obtain a number of successes
differing from the expected value by an amount exceeding $\lambda\sigma$.

Case c: p and q are both positive.

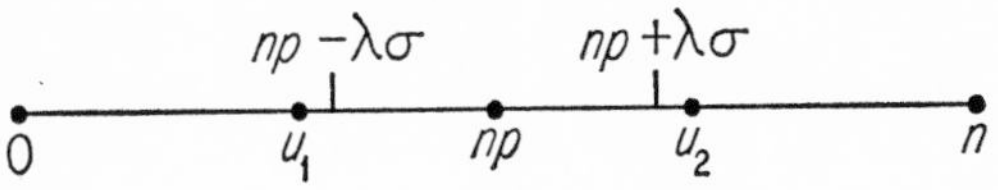

FIGURE 18

We wish to discover the probability that r, the number of
successes, falls outside of the interval $[np - \lambda\sigma, np + \lambda\sigma]$. If
u_1 is the greatest integer less than $np - \lambda\sigma$ and u_2 is the smallest
integer greater than $np + \lambda\sigma$, then we wish to show the
following:

$$\sum_{r=0}^{u_1} {}_nC_r p^r q^{n-r} + \sum_{r=u_2}^{n} {}_nC_r p^r q^{n-r} < \frac{1}{\lambda^2}$$

By the definition of variance and using the fact that $\sigma^2 = npq$,
we have

$$\sum_{r=0}^{u_1} (np - r)^2 {}_nC_r p^r q^{n-r} + \sum_{r=u_1}^{u_2} (np - r)^2 {}_nC_r p^r q^{n-r}$$
$$+ \sum_{r=u_2}^{n} (np - r)^2 {}_nC_r p^r q^{n-r} = npq$$

For all values of r less than or equal to u_1, $|np - r| > \lambda\sigma$, as appears from the diagram above. By the same reasoning, we have that for all values of r greater than or equal to u_2 $|np - r| > \lambda\sigma$. Therefore,

$$\sum_{r=0}^{u_1} (np - r)^2 {}_nC_r p^r q^{n-r} + \sum_{r=u_2}^{n} (np - r)^2 {}_nC_r p^r q^{n-r} >$$

$$\lambda^2\sigma^2 \Big[\sum_{r=0}^{u_1} {}_nC_r p^r q^{n-r} + \sum_{r=u_2}^{n} {}_nC_r p^r q^{n-r} \Big]$$

Hence,

$$\lambda^2\sigma^2 \Big[\sum_{r=0}^{u_1} {}_nC_r p^r q^{n-r} + \sum_{r=u_2}^{n} {}_nC_r p^r q^{n-r} \Big] < \sigma^2$$

Dividing through on both sides of the inequality by $\lambda^2\sigma^2$, we obtain

$$\sum_{r=0}^{u_1} {}_nC_r p^r q^{n-r} + \sum_{r=u_2}^{n} {}_nC_r p^r q^{n-r} < \frac{1}{\lambda^2}$$

The reader will perceive that the left side of this inequality signifies the probability of obtaining a number of successes deviating from the most probable number by an amount greater than $\lambda\sigma$. In other words, we have proved that in a Bernoulli sequence of size n the probability is less than $1/\lambda^2$ that the number of successes will deviate from the most probable value by an amount greater than $\lambda\sigma$.

EXERCISE

1 What is the probability in a series of 400 throws of a fair coin that one will obtain between 150 and 250 heads?

Assuming the sequence to be Bernoullian, the most probable number of successes is 200. We wish the probablity of obtaining a deviation from the most probable number which does not exceed the value, 50. Here

$$50 = \lambda \sqrt{npq} = \lambda \sqrt{400 \cdot \tfrac{1}{4}} = 10\lambda$$

So

$$\lambda = 5 \quad \text{and} \quad 1/\lambda^2 = \tfrac{1}{25} = 0.04$$

The probability is less than 4 per cent that one will obtain a deviation greater than 50 from the most probable number. Therefore, the probability must exceed 96 per cent that one will obtain a deviation no greater than 50. In general, in Bernoulli sequences, the probability of a deviation no greater than $\lambda\sigma$ is greater than $1 - 1/\lambda^2$.

The Law of Large Numbers

To say that $np - \lambda\sigma \leqslant r \leqslant np + \lambda\sigma$ is equivalent to saying that

$$p - \frac{\lambda\sigma}{n} \leqslant f \leqslant p + \frac{\lambda\sigma}{n}$$

where r is the number of successes in a Bernoulli sequence of size n, p is the probability of success, and f is the relative frequency r/n with which successes occur in the sequence.

We wish now to prove that in a Bernoulli sequence of size n the probability is less than or equal to pq/nd^2 that the success ratio f will differ from the probability p by an amount exceeding d, where d is greater than 0.

Case a: $p = 0$, $q = 1$.

The probability, in this case, of a deviation exceeding d must equal or be less than the probability of obtaining either one success or two successes or three successes or ... or n successes. In view of the zero value of p, this probability must be zero. Hence, when p is zero, the probability is clearly equal to pq/nd^2 that one will obtain a relative frequency differing from p by an amount exceeding d.

Case b: $p = 1$, $q = 0$.

The probability, in this case, of a deviation exceeding d must equal or be less than the probability of obtaining one failure or two failures or three failures or ... or n failures. In view of the zero value of q, this probability must be zero. Hence, when q is zero, the probability is equal to pq/nd^2 that one will obtain a relative frequency differing from p by an amount exceeding d.

Case c: p and q both exceed zero.

We know that the probability is less than $1/\lambda^2$ that f will differ from p by an amount greater than $\lambda\sigma/n$, and the probability is greater than $1 - 1/\lambda^2$ that f will differ from p by an amount not exceeding $\lambda\sigma/n$. If we put d equal to $\lambda\sigma/n$, then

$$\lambda = \frac{nd}{\sigma} \quad \text{and} \quad 1/\lambda^2 = \frac{pq}{nd^2}$$

Hence, when p and q are each positive, the probability must be less than pq/nd^2 that the success ratio will differ from p by an amount exceeding d. And whatever the value of p, the probability cannot exceed pq/nd^2 that the success ratio will differ from p by an amount greater than d. Since pq/nd^2 becomes small when n increases, it follows that the probability of a deviation between f and p, which is greater than d, is as small as you like for sufficiently large values of n. This is the law of large numbers. It should be realized that the law of large numbers does not predict what the relative frequency will be. It tells us only that a deviation of specified magnitude from the probability is highly improbable in sufficiently large samples. Furthermore, nothing has been said to indicate just how improbable a deviation is. All that has been established is that the probability is less than or equal to pq/nd^2 that the deviation will be greater than d. However, mathematicians have developed methods for approximating more accurately the values of such probabilities in cases where direct calculation is impracticable. Thus, it is known that the probability is close to 68 per cent that the success ratio in a Bernoulli sequence of size n will differ from the probability of success by an amount not exceeding σ/n. The probability is close to 95 per cent that the success ratio will differ from the probability by an amount not exceeding $2\sigma/n$. The probability is close to 99 per cent that the success ratio will deviate from the probability by an amount no greater than $3\sigma/n$.

6

Inductive Inference

1. We have seen that, in a Bernoulli sequence of n independent trials with constant probability of success, the probability exceeds or equals $1 - pq/nd^2$ that the empirical success ratio will differ from p, the probability of an individual success, by an amount no greater than d. For fixed n and d, what is the minimal value of $1 - pq/nd^2$? Evidently, $1 - pq/nd^2$ has a minimum when pq/nd^2 has a maximum value. And pq/nd^2 has a maximum value, for fixed n and d, when the product pq is a maximum. Now p plus q equals 1, for all values of p. Hence, by an elementary application of the differential calculus, we see that pq is a maximum when $p = q$. In other words, $1 - pq/nd^2$ has a minimal value when success and failure are equally likely.

It follows from the foregoing that in a Bernoulli sequence of n trials, *whatever* the probability of an individual success, the probability must *exceed* $1 - 1/4nd^2$ that the probability of an individual success and the success ratio of the sample will differ by an amount no greater than d.

If either p or q is zero, then the probability is unity (and so greater than $1 - 1/4nd^2$) that the difference between p and the success ratio will be no greater than d. If p and q are positive, then the probability of a deviation no greater than d must exceed, we have seen, $1 - pq/nd^2$. But the lowest value of $1 - pq/nd^2$ is $1 - 1/4nd^2$. It therefore follows that, whatever the value of p, in a Bernoulli sequence the probability must exceed $1 - 1/4nd^2$ that the deviation between the probability and the success ratio will be no greater than d, where d is any positive quantity. Put less exactly: for large n, it is very probable, in such sequences, that the success ratio will approximate the probability of success in a single trial.

2. Closely connected with the idea of probability is the concept of reasonable expectation, which may be explained in the following way:

If we estimate the probability to be u that an object selected by a certain method will have a property F, then u also measures our reasonable expectation, the expectation to which we are entitled, that a specific object selected by that method will have that property F, provided that we have no other information whose relevance we are in a position to ascertain.

Thus, if a regular Bernoullian die were thrown a great many times and we estimated that the probability of obtaining an ace on any trial was $\frac{1}{6}$, then it would be a reasonable expectation that the proportion of aces thrown in that particular series would be nearly $\frac{1}{6}$, there being no other information known to be relevant and available to us.

It follows that if we assume a sequence of trials to be Bernoullian, our reasonable expectation should be very great that the success ratio will nearly equal the probability of success in a single trial, provided that n is great and no other information is known to be relevant.

It also follows from the assumption of Bernoullian trials that when n is large we may, with a highly reasonable expectation of being right, infer the approximate value of the probability of a single success from the success ratio encountered in the n trials, if there is no other evidence known to be relevant.

It is important to be clear about the reasoning which is involved here. We know that if M is a Bernoullian method of selection generating a sequence of n independent trials in each of which the probability of success is constant, then the probability must exceed $1 - 1/4nd^2$ that such a sequence will possess a success ratio f satisfying the condition, $|p - f| \leqslant d$, where p

is the probability of an individual success. If we assume all this, then our degree of *reasonable expectation* must also exceed $1 - 1/4nd^2$ that *this particular sequence* has a success ratio differing from p by an amount no greater than d. If n is appropriately large, we may say, in the light of our assumptions and with no other relevant information, that it is highly reasonable to expect, *in this case*, that $|p - f| \leqslant d$. If, then, f is known, we may, with reasonable expectation of being right, infer that p differs from f by an amount no greater than d. This type of inference may be regarded as a special type of induction. It consists in inferring an approximate value of a probability from an observed ratio. It is a highly cogent form of inference, requiring the premiss that the distribution of probabilities is Bernoullian and requiring also that no other information available be known to be relevant. Not all cogent inductive inference, however, conforms to this pattern.

3. *Random sampling from large populations*

Let P be a population containing N elements, R of which are of the sort F, $N - R$ of the sort non-F. We draw a random sample of n elements. What is the probability that r of the sample are F's? The total number of combinations of size n which can be formed is $_NC_n$. The number of these which are favorable is $_RC_r \cdot _{N-R}C_{n-r}$. Hence, our probability is

$$\frac{_RC_r \cdot _{N-R}C_{n-r}}{NC_n}$$

We shall show that if R, N, and $N - R$ become infinite and n, r, and $n - r$ are fixed, our probability approaches $_nC_r p^r q^{n-r}$ as a limit, where p is R/N and q is $(N - R)/N$.

Consider the ratio

$$\frac{_uP_v}{u^v} = \frac{u}{u} \cdot \frac{u-1}{u} \cdot \ldots \cdot \frac{u - (v-1)}{u}$$

$$= 1 \cdot \left(1 - \frac{1}{u}\right) \cdot \left(1 - \frac{2}{u}\right) \cdot \ldots \cdot \left(1 - \frac{v-1}{u}\right)$$

If $u \to \infty$ and v is fixed, obviously

$$\frac{_uP_v}{u^v} \to 1$$

Now consider

$$\frac{{}_RC_r \cdot {}_{N-R}C_{n-r}}{{}_NC_n} = \frac{\dfrac{{}_RP_r}{r!R^r} \cdot \dfrac{{}_{N-R}P_{n-r}}{(n-r)!(N-R)^{n-r}} \cdot \dfrac{R^r \cdot (N-R)^{n-r}}{N^n}}{\dfrac{{}_nP_n}{n!N^n}}$$

This approximates, as N, R, and $N - R$ become large, to

$$\frac{n!}{r!(n-r)!} \cdot \frac{R^r \cdot (N-R)^{n-r}}{N^n}$$

which is

$$ {}_nC_r \cdot \left(\frac{R}{N}\right)^r \cdot \left(\frac{N-R}{N}\right)^{n-r} $$

or ${}_nC_r p^r q^{n-r}$, where p is the probability of selecting an F at random and $q = 1 - p$. In other words, in random sampling from a large population, the probability of obtaining a certain number of successes may be approximated by using the Bernoullian distribution.*

It follows by the law of large numbers that if we draw a sample of size n at random from a virtually infinite population, the probability may be taken to exceed $1 - 1/4nd^2$ that the success ratio of the sample will differ from the success ratio of the population by an amount no greater than d. Hence, if we assume that our population is very large and our method of selection random, our reasonable expectation is great that the composition of our sample will agree with the composition of the population, if n is moderately large and no other relevant information is to be considered. In other words, it is reasonable to consider a random sample as a representative sample if the population is very large and the sample not too small.

Induction is a procedure whereby a probability may be inferred from an observed sample ratio. We cannot justify such a procedure by mathematics alone. However, the theory of probability enables us to understand the structure of the argument by which induction provides us with a reasonable expectation of success. We have already seen that when we assume that a sequence of trials satisfies Bernoullian require-

* See Neyman, J., *First Course In Probability and Statistics*. New York: Henry Holt, 1950, p. 211.

ments, the sample ratio may provide us with a probable index of the probability of an individual success. Hence, induction (of the type presently under consideration) may be justified in terms of an underlying hypothesis to the effect that a series of experiments is Bernoullian or approximately Bernoullian. But the question must be faced: how may we justify the hypothesis that a series of trials are independent and that the probability of success is constant in that series?

4. In certain cases, we have seen, we can measure probabilities with reasonable precision by determining the relative frequency with which certain events have occurred, provided we assume as an underlying hypothesis that the events have occurred under approximately Bernoullian conditions. However, it is necessary now to consider what sort of justification can be provided for the acceptance or rejection of hypotheses. For example, what justification do we have for assuming that a method of sampling is random? No doubt, if our sampling has been random, past observation does show that the probability is 1 that a man is mortal. But that our methods of sampling are random is more difficult to establish than the simple proposition that all men are mortal. Again, the proposition that the center of the earth is fluid is a hypothesis whose truth or falsity is not determined by random sampling from a population consisting of earth bodies.

5. It is obvious that when a hypothesis has been tested, we seek in the most reasonable way to determine its truth value on the basis of the outcome of tests performed. The rationale of such determination of truth values is a problem concerning the application of the theory of probability.

At this point, it is well to remind ourselves that probability pertains to general kinds of things and not to individual things themselves. Thus we may speak of the probability that an object selected from G will be of such and such a sort. Here it is presupposed that the operation of selection may be repeated indefinitely. Also, the probability is always the probability, in relation to a definite method of selection, that a certain repeatable feature will be exemplified in a selected object.

Let G be a set of hypotheses which are testable. Let M, the method of selection, consist of formulating a hypothesis of G and then testing it. The probability of selecting a true hypothesis from G by the method M is written

$$P(M, G, T)$$

which we abbreviate, according to our general practice, as

$$P(T)$$

We shall assume that $P(T)$ exceeds 0, in the case of a particular G and M which are in question.

6. In any investigation there is a body of information presupposed which is unquestioned in that investigation. No doubt, what is presupposed in one investigation may be questioned in another. But since we restrict ourselves to a particular investigation, we may take the information presupposed by that investigation as a constant, K. And we shall assume that K consists of true propositions. Our problem is, assuming that K is true, what may be inferred from K as to the truth or falsity of the hypotheses in G, when nothing may strictly be deduced from K which is logically decisive as to the truth or falsity of these hypotheses.

7. Before attempting to deal with this question, we must first explain what the meaning of confirmation is and how that meaning is connected with the parameter, K.

Suppose that a particular hypothesis, h, in conjunction with all the relevant information in K, permits us to infer, with high probability, a particular experimental outcome. Then the occurrence of such an outcome confirms the hypothesis h, unless K by itself provides an equally strong basis for predicting that outcome. For example, our hypothesis may be that the tosses with a coin conform to Bernoullian requirements and that the probability is $\frac{1}{2}$ that heads will occur on any trial. Then, we have seen, it is very probable in a large sequence of trials that nearly $\frac{1}{2}$ will be heads. This outcome would confirm the Bernoullian hypothesis, unless we had in K other means of making the same, or a more precise, forecast with at least an equal probability coefficient. Accordingly, whether a hypothesis is confirmed by an experimental outcome depends upon and is relative to the content of K.

However, suppose that a hypothesis, in conjunction with all the relevant information in K, permits us to infer, with high probability, a particular experimental outcome which is not equally predictable on the basis of K alone; then the non-occurrence of that outcome is said to disconfirm the hypothesis.

We are here assuming that there is a positive probability in relation to the system, $[M, G]$, that a selected hypothesis is true, and we are construing the operation M as the operation of formulating and testing a member of G. Here, testing is an operation which results in the confirmation or disconfirmation of a hypothesis.

Let $P(C, T)$ be the conditional probability that a hypothesis selected from G is true, granted that it confirmed. Then by the multiplication rule we have:

$$P(C, T) = \frac{P(T) \cdot P(T, C)}{P(C)} = \frac{P(T) \cdot P(T, C)}{P(CT \vee CF)}$$

$$= \frac{P(T) \cdot P(T, C)}{P(CT) + P(CF)}$$

$$= \frac{1}{1 + \dfrac{P(F)}{P(T)} \cdot \dfrac{P(F, C)}{P(T, C)}}$$

Our data do not permit us to evaluate the ratio, $P(F)/P(T)$, but it follows from our assumptions that it has a positive value.

Accordingly, the value of $P(C, T)$ depends upon the ratio $P(F, C)/P(T, C)$. As that ratio diminishes, $P(C, T)$ increases. Now the laws of probability do not of themselves permit us to evaluate this ratio, and it is impossible on the basis of mathematics alone to decide how probable it is that a confirmed proposition is true. We evidently need some additional assumption which pure mathematics cannot supply.

8. The student will notice that false statements are quite frequently confirmed and that there is nothing obviously improbable about the confirmation of falsehoods. Nevertheless, we are, if we are empiricists, persuaded that there is a discoverable difference between truth and falsity, so we are constrained to look deeper and to formulate if we can, some probability connection between the ideas of truth, falsity, and disconfirmation.

We are construing G as the class of testable hypotheses which we humans select from and test. It is perfectly true that we are not able to determine how probable it is that a false hypothesis selected from G will be confirmed. But we do normally suppose that confirmation is less probable in the case of a falsehood than in the case of a truth. We are not here discussing any particular hypothesis. We are merely saying of hypotheses in general that it is less probable that a falsehood will be confirmed than it is that a truth will be confirmed and we also, such is our postulate, assume that the disparity between these probabilities increases as our tests become more demanding and numerous.

If confirmation is as likely in the case of falsehood as in the case of truth, then there is no purpose in testing. But if our disparity postulate is accepted, if it is granted that as our tests are more numerous and varied, then the ratio $P(F, C)/P(T, C)$ diminishes, then it is evident from the multiplication rule that as our tests are more numerous and varied, the probability that a confirmed hypothesis is true must increase.

We may state our assumption somewhat differently. The probability that a falsehood will be confirmed is more sensitive to an increase in the severity of our tests than is the probability that a true hypothesis will be confirmed.

According to the point of view here expressed, the justification of scientific procedure is not that our tests are presently known to establish the truth of hypotheses. It is, rather, that the continued process of intensifying the severity of our tests is bound eventually to produce a condition in which confirmation is a highly probable index of truth.

To summarize what we have said: we do not know how probable it is that a hypothesis tested is true. If we are so constituted that we *never* think to test true hypotheses, then neither the study of probability nor anything else will do us any good. But if there is a positive probability that a hypothesis selected is true, then the ratio $P(F)/P(T)$ is positive. Hence $P(C, T)$ is seen to depend on the ratio

$$P(F, C)/P(T, C)$$

Now, our assumption is that false propositions are, in general, less likely to be confirmed than true ones and that the comparative improbability of confirmation in the case of falsehoods increases with the severity of our tests. Consequently, the probability that a confirmation betokens truth must approximate certainty as our tests increase in complexity, variety, and severity.

Now, the assumption of the disparity between $P(F, C)$ and $P(T, C)$ is not a mathematically necessary proposition, demonstrable in the calculus of probability, nor is it itself an empirical hypothesis to be inferred from its confirmation in experience. For we have seen that any high estimate of $P(C, T)$, when it is reasonable, presupposes the assumption of the disparity between the probability of confirmation in the case of true hypotheses and the probability of confirmation in the case of false hypotheses.

The same disparity assumption occurs in the inference from the disconfirmation of a hypothesis to its falsity. By the multiplication rule we have

$$P(D, F) = \cfrac{1}{1 + \cfrac{P(T)}{P(F)} \cdot \cfrac{P(T, D)}{P(F, D)}}$$

where D is the property of being disconfirmed.

It is true that $P(T, D)$ must be small, but so might $P(F, D)$, so far as pure mathematics is concerned. We need to assume that $P(T, D)$ is less than $P(F, D)$ and that the disparity increases with the severity of our tests. Now this assumption is equivalent to the one already made, since

$$P(T, D) = 1 - P(T, C)$$

and

$$P(F, D) = 1 - P(F, C)$$

It follows that we cannot reasonably infer the falsity of the disparity principle from a disconfirmation, since the disparity principle is a presupposition underlying that type of inference also. The disparity principle is neither proved by empirical confirmation nor refutable by empirical disconfirmation. It appears to be an assumption in the absence of which we should be able to make no reasonable determination of the truth values of hypotheses on the basis of experience.

It is true that in practice we are unable to give a reliable estimate of the probability that a confirmed hypothesis is a true one. As we have seen, we can only reasonably maintain that in the advance of experience a degree of confirmation must eventually be achieved which is a highly probable indication of truth.

However, the disparity principle does not call for a mystical act of faith. Let us consider what would be the case if

$$\frac{P(F, C)}{P(T, C)} = 1$$

Then obviously,

$$P(C, T) = \frac{1}{1 + \frac{P(T)}{P(F)}} = \frac{P(T)}{P(F) + P(T)} = P(T)$$

In this case C and T are irrelevant to one another. Hence,

$$P(T, C) = \frac{P(C) \cdot P(C, T)}{P(T)} = \frac{P(C) \cdot P(T)}{P(T)} = P(C)$$

But $P(T, C)$ is very close to 1. Hence, the probability that a hypothesis will be confirmed must also be close to 1. Hence, we have shown that if $P(F, C) = P(T, C)$ then $P(C)$ must be very great.

Now we do not need to design our experiments so as to have $P(C)$ great. It is possible to design our experiments so that $P(C)$ will be small. Before we explain this point, let us see what effect diminishing $P(C)$ will have on the ratio

$$\frac{P(F, C)}{P(T, C)}$$

$C = [C \cdot T \vee C \cdot F]$. Since $C \cdot T$ and $C \cdot F$ are exclusive properties,

$$P(C) = P(C \cdot T) + P(C \cdot F)$$
$$= P(T) \cdot P(T, C) + P(F) \cdot P(F, C)$$

Hence,

$$P(F, C) = \frac{P(C) - P(T) \cdot P(T, C)}{P(F)}$$

$$= \frac{P(C) - P(T) \cdot P(T, C)}{1 - P(T)}$$

Now $P(T, C)$ is near to unity. If $P(C)$ is diminished so as to approach $P(T) \cdot P(T, C)$, $P(F, C)$ must also diminish and approach the value, 0. Hence, by reducing $P(C)$ we also reduce the ratio, $P(F, C)/P(T, C)$, and in this way we also increase the value of $P(C, T)$. Our problem, then, is how to design our experiments so that $P(C)$ will be very small or, in other words, how to design experiments so that the probability will be very great that we shall obtain disconfirmations.

A little reflection about scientific as well as ordinary practice will give us the answer. We are commonly told that science characteristically devises and tests hypotheses and, ever discontented, devises alternative hypotheses and tests these, too. Indeed, it is characteristic that the scientist designs his experiments in order to test a large group of alternative hypotheses in such a way that most of them, if not all, will be disconfirmed.

It is quite proper to insist, following Popper, that the greatest emphasis should be placed upon the role of disconfirmation, in the process of testing. Scientific procedure is an attempt to formulate and test severely as many alternative hypotheses as human imagination can contrive. The process of confirming hypotheses lives in and through the operation of disconfirmation. A hypothesis which is corroborated in isolation is not "severely tested". If our standard is to multiply alternative hypotheses and vary our tests so as to disconfirm at least a large majority of the alternatives, then the effect must be, in consequence of this severe standard of testing, that *the proportion of disconfirmations must greatly exceed the proportion of confirmations* and, consequently, we have the result that the more severe is our standard of testing, the less likely it is that hypotheses will be confirmed; and, the more severe our standard of testing, the more probable it is that a confirmed hypothesis is true.

Science considers as many alternative theories as it can. It is, in general, not possible to consider all of the possible alternatives to a given theory. But it is necessary to the scientific method that alternative possibilities of explanation be explored as fully as our knowledge permits and that our confirmations of hypotheses be linked with the disconfirmation of most, at least, of the known alternatives. In this way, our adoption of a severe standard of criticism and of testing must inevitably lead to a guarantee that the probability of a confirmation is small. It is this attitude of hospitality towards the consideration of many alternative possibilities and the commitment to apply the most severe methods of testing which must eventually ensure a high probability for scientific inferences.

Just how severe must our testing be? Obviously, there is no answer possible to this question. What we know is that scientific inquiry, as it increases the severity of its test procedures, must inevitably arrive at a condition in which confirmation betokens truth.

To be sure, there is an economic limitation upon open-mindedness. Life is short and curiosity is long. To embark upon new inquiries, we must terminate some other inquiries. One must plan the use of one's time. If someone advances a new system of physics which tolerates the possibility of a perpetual motion machine, no scientist today will spend a moment of his time upon it. There are other and more promising investigations to enter upon. Hence, there are matters which are closed, inquiries which are terminated, conclusions which are drawn. But lest dogmatists draw comfort from this fact, one must also say that it is, in principle, possible for new facts to be encountered or new theories to be corroborated which may well call for a fresh consideration of time-honored certainties. The door is shut but not irretrievably locked.

9. Science is an attempt to formulate simple explanatory hypotheses and laws which are systematically connected and which have numerous and varied confirmations.

It is characteristic of science not merely to develop such hypotheses but to develop as many promising alternatives as possible and to select from these alternatives those which are the most highly confirmed, rejecting those which are disconfirmed. The process of acceptance and rejection of hypotheses is provisional and tentative. A hypothesis which is rejected at one time may call for reinstatement at another. And a hypothesis which is provisionally accepted at one time may subsequently be disconfirmed and, therefore, rejected.

The provisional character of scientific inference is justified by the circumstance that hypotheses are contingent, indemonstrable, and corrigible in the light of new experience. But the provisional character of scientific assertion must not be misunderstood to mean that science asserts nothing. It means that science is prepared to revise its assertions in the face of new experience, in order to achieve greater explanatory force and higher confirmation for its statements.

There are those who fear to subject certain beliefs to scientific scrutiny. Such persons should be reminded that their fears are misplaced. If their beliefs are true, the probability must be very great that they will be corroborated, and hence provisionally accepted. If science errs, it is on the side of charity. If these people believe in the truth of their beliefs (and if they don't, they don't have belief), they are unreasonable in protecting their beliefs from scientific examination.

A critic of scientific method may admit that it is very probable that true propositions will be corroborated, yet he may call attention to the fact that false propositions may be corroborated also. Hence, he may argue, we have no warrant to infer that a proposition is true from the premiss that it has been corroborated. The point is well taken. Our answer has already been indicated in our enunciation of the disparity principle. The policy of considering a large number of alternatives to a given hypothesis and devising tests so that only a small proportion of confirmations is obtainable has the consequence that false propositions are not as likely to be confirmed as true ones and, therefore, that confirmed propositions are likely to be true. Indeed, the process of ever increasing the number, variety, and severity of our tests must inevitably result in a condition in which it is nearly certain that confirmation betokens truth.

Is it conceivable that there should be a policy which is

superior to the policy which we have described? Evidently, if there were, its reliability could be tested. If its reliability were strongly confirmed, we should accept it as if it were a new law of nature. It would not, therefore, be a genuine alternative to scientific policy but a particular application of it.

10. We are now in a position to understand how the Bernoullian character of certain methods of selection may be scientifically warranted. We may use the example of coin tossing. We begin by considering the hypothesis that coin tossing is an example of a Bernoullian method of selection and that the attribute heads has a probability of nearly $\frac{1}{2}$. Using the law of large numbers, we may predict with high probability what, approximately, the ratio of heads will be in a large sample, if our hypothesis is true. If the observed proportion of heads falls within the designated interval of approximation, the hypothesis is confirmed. Otherwise, the hypothesis is disconfirmed.

But, as has been pointed out, it is necessary not merely to confirm our hypothesis but to amass an amount and variety of evidence which will disconfirm a great variety of alternative hypotheses. For example, we may test the hypothesis that coin tossing is Bernoullian but that the probability of heads is $\frac{9}{10}$. We may test the hypothesis that the probability of heads depends on the weather, the day of the week, the state of mind of the observer and so on. We may consider the possibility that a coin will systematically compensate for a long run of heads by producing a long run of tails. The elimination of a variety of alternative hypotheses as well as the confirmation of the originally formulated hypothesis is essential to the underlying technique of science which when systematically applied supports the common expectation that the confirmation of an hypothesis is a relatively unlikely event and that the confirmation of a false hypothesis is even more unlikely.

Bibliography

Black, M., *Critical Thinking*, second ed. Englewood Cliffs, N. J.: Prentice-Hall, Inc., 1952.

Braithwaite, R. B., *Scientific Explanation*. New York: Cambridge University Press, 1953.

Church, Alonzo, *Introduction to Mathematical Logic*. Princeton, N. J.: Princeton University Press, 1956.

Cohen, M. R. and E. Nagel, *An Introduction to Logic and Scientific Method*. New York: Harcourt, Brace & Company, 1934.

Cooley, John, *A Primer of Formal Logic*. New York: Macmillan Company, 1949.

Eaton, R., *General Logic*. New York: Charles Scribner's Sons, 1931.

Lewis, C. I., *A Survey of Symbolic Logic*. Berkeley: University of California Press, 1918.

Lewis, C. I., and C. H. Langford, *Symbolic Logic*. New York: Appleton-Century-Crofts, Inc., 1932.

Nagel, E., "Principles of the Theory of Probability," *International Encyclopedia of Unified Science*. Chicago: University of Chicago Press, 1939, Vol. I, No. 6.

Neyman, J., *First Course in Probability and Statistics*. New York: Henry Holt & Company, Inc., 1950.

Quine, W. V., *Methods of Logic*, revised ed. New York: Henry Holt & Company, Inc., 1959.

———, *Mathematical Logic*, revised ed. Cambridge, Mass.: Harvard University Press, 1951.

Stebbing, L. S., *A Modern Introduction to Logic*. London: Methuen & Co., Ltd., 1930.

Popper, Karl, *The Logic of Scientific Discovery*. London: Hutchinson & Co., Ltd., 1959.

Williams, Donald, *The Ground of Induction*. Cambridge, Mass.: Harvard University Press, 1947.

Index